Green and Gold

GREEN and GOLD

STORIES AND POEMS FROM BENGAL

EDITED BY HUMAYUN KABIR

ASSOCIATE EDITORS:

TARASANKAR BANERJEE

PREMENDRA MITRA

A NEW DIRECTIONS BOOK

NEW DIRECTIONS BOOKS ARE PUBLISHED AT NORFOLK, CONNECTICUT,
BY JAMES LAUGHLIN. NEW YORK ADDRESS: 333 SIXTH AVENUE (14)

PRINTED IN INDIA
BY Z. T. BANDUKWALA AT LEADERS' PRESS PRIVATE LTD., BOMBAY

For

BIDHAN CHANDRA ROY

Physician, Statesman and Practical Idealist

Contents

*Translated by the author

vii

*Translated by the author

Preface

THIS volume is the first of a series intended to introduce some of the contemporary writers of India to the world outside. Of the fourteen languages recognised in the Constitution of India, Sanskrit occupies a unique position as a classical language of world-wide importance. The other thirteen are spoken by millions of people and have living literatures with histories stretching back many centuries. They have all exhibited a remarkable vitality and strength since the impact of the West ushered in the Indian renaissance.

Some of the earlier writers of modern India have been translated into European languages and have secured for themselves a world audience. Of them the most notable is Rabindranath Tagore, but there have been others who have deservedly won the admiration of the outside world. Apart from these few exceptions, the majority of Indian writers are hardly known outside their own linguistic areas. This not only restricts their field of readers but is also an obstacle to better understanding among different sections of the Indian people and between India and the outside world.

The first volume in the series is a selection of writings from Bengali, which is perhaps the richest of the modern Indian languages. It is proposed to follow up with similar selections from writings in Hindi, Tamil, Telugu, Marathi, Gujarati, and the other Indian languages. It is hoped that the publication of these anthologies will not only make the world outside conscious of the vitality and strength of the literary tradition in the different Indian languages but also help to draw the

different language groups closer to one another by creating
the corpus of a common Indian literature for all. It is my
belief that once the series is completed, it will be recognised
that contemporary India has writers who in richness of experience and fineness of perception are not inferior to their
compeers anywhere in the world.

The stories and poems have been selected jointly by a com-
mittee consisting of Mr. Tarasankar Banerjee, Mr. Premendra
Mitra and the Editor. The editors have in most cases selected pieces according to the wishes of the writer himself, but
they are fully conscious of the fact that many fine pieces of
writing have been left out. They are also aware that some
pieces selected by them may be regarded as less satisfactory
than others not included. In art, there can be no finality
in judgment and least of all in respect of contemporary
writing. The only anthology that is completely satisfactory
is the one that each man makes for himself.

In making selections for this anthology, the choice has been
restricted to writers who have made a mark in the last twenty-
five years or so. Almost all of them are living, and some of
them are still young. The editors recognise that there may
be differences of opinion about both the inclusion and the
exclusion of individual writers and writings. They can only
say that they have made their selections after consulting
some of the most well-known literary figures and critics of
modern Bengal. The final decision was however theirs and
they must take the responsibility for their choice.

The poems and stories have been arranged alphabetically
according to the names of the authors. Some of them have
been translated by the authors themselves and are indicated
by an asterisk in the table of contents. The others are the work
of a group of translators consisting of Mrs. Lila Ray and
Messrs. Benoy Chaudhury, Amalendu Das Gupta, Chidananda
Das Gupta, Zahiruddin Ahmad, Chanchal Sarkar and the
Editor.

I must deeply thank Dr. B. C. Roy, Chief Minister of West

Bengal and one of the outstanding statesmen of contemporary
India, for the encouragement and assistance received from
him in the preparation of this work. He sanctioned a grant by
the Government of West Bengal to meet the expenses of
collecting the stories and poems, purchasing their translation
rights, and other editorial work. Dr. D. M. Sen has also taken
a keen interest in the preparation and publication of the
book. Thanks are due to the writers and translators without
whose co-operation the work would not have been accomplished. I would also like to thank Mr. Atawar Rahman for
his help in collecting and editing the manuscripts.

HUMAYUN KABIR

New Delhi,
November 14, 1956

Introduction

E V E N a few decades ago India was hardly more than a name to a majority of men and women in most countries of the world. They thought of her, if at all, as a vast country somewhere in distant Asia peopled by maharajas and faqirs, tigers and serpents and full of the mystery and magic of the ageless East. With the attainment of independence, India has become more real to millions in all the continents. Names like Tagore and Gandhi, Nehru and Radhakrishnan are slowly becoming familiar at least to the educated classes. Even they do not always realise the richness and length of India's history nor the cultural, religious and linguistic variety which has characterised India since immemorial times. Such ignorance, or worse, indifference is not compatible with the growing interlacing of human relations and the increasing condensation of the world in space and time. A world that is being inexorably unified demands that people in all countries should know more and more about their neighbours on this terrestrial globe.

If India is herself only a name for millions in Africa, America and Europe, it is not surprising that there should be still less knowledge or understanding of her constituent units. Those who have heard of India do not always know that she is a subcontinent divided into a number of regions speaking different languages. Still fewer know that each of these regions is as large as many European countries and there are a dozen major languages, each spoken by millions and with literatures that go back many centuries.

Perhaps the easiest and most fruitful way of attaining understanding between peoples of all countries is through knowledge

of one another's literature, art and philosophy. Art uses universal symbols which transcend the barriers of language.
Literature speaks to depths of experience where differences due
to customs and conventions are overcome. Philosophy seeks
truths which are the same for all. Deeper cultural understanding among the peoples of the world can be best achieved if we
seek to advance simultaneously on all these fronts.

I

A M O N G the major languages of India, Bengali which is
represented in the present volume has perhaps the richest
and most vigorous literary tradition. People in distant regions
have heard of the city of Calcutta but not many know that it
is the capital of West Bengal, one of the constituent units of
the Indian Union. Fewer still know that Bengali is spoken by
about seventy-five million men and women and understood by
another twenty to thirty million. It is the language not only of
West Bengal in the Indian Union but also of the eastern wing
of the Republic of Pakistan. In fact, speakers of Bengali
constitute the largest single linguistic group in Pakistan and
Bengali has been recognised as one of the official languages of
that Republic. Distributed in India and Pakistan, Bengali can
thus claim the status of an international language on political
grounds. That claim is also justified on artistic and literary
considerations.

The earliest history of Bengal is shrouded in mystery. It is
mentioned in the *Mahabharata* and already appears as a land
comparatively free from social and religious orthodoxy. From
the mass of legends, fables and traditions which have come
down the ages, it is clear that Bengal was one of the regions
least affected by the impact of the Aryan invasion. Nor is this
surprising. Located in the north-eastern corner of India, the
Aryans had to cross the entire sub-continent before they
reached it. They also met with stiff opposition from the local
people who were a mixture of Dravidians, Mongolians and

aboriginals. Nor did the Aryans find the climate congenial, for it is warm and humid except for a brief spell of winter in December and January. The Aryan attitude towards this border land in the far-eastern region of India is expressed in their description of it as the *Pandava Varjita Desha*—the land beyond the pale of Pandava (or Aryan) rule.

Nothing definite is known of the history of Bengal till the seventh century after Christ. There are reasons to think that Bengal was deeply influenced by the teachings of the Buddha who was born on its borders about six hundred years before Christ. By that time, the Aryan settlement of India was almost complete and the simple religion of the Vedas had given place to the rituals and forms associated with Brahminism. The Brahminic influence was however never deep in Bengal and the people found little difficulty in shaking it off in favour of Buddhism which repudiated caste and ritual. The first historic empire in India was established by Chandragupta Maurya soon after Alexander's invasion. Chandragupta's capital was near modern Patna close to the borders of Bengal and one may easily assume that Bengal shared in the general prosperity brought about by the establishment of the empire. Flourishing sea ports grew up in its coastal towns and one of them, *Tamralipti*, became famous as the centre from which Asoka—grandson of Chandragupta and one of the noblest kings the world has known—sent his missions of peace to carry the Buddha's message to all parts of the then known world. Trade and commerce prospered and Bengal became well known for its artistic products even at this early period.

Buddhism remained the dominant religion of Bengal till about the ninth century after Christ. Many kingdoms and empires flourished and decayed during this period but the life of the people flowed in traditional channels. Villages had a large degree of autonomy and managed most of their local affairs. So long as the king received his annual dues, he did not interfere with the life of the villager. Maintenance of law and order and the administration of justice were both local con-

cerns. The fertility of the land and the warm and humid climate
did not encourage a hard and strenuous life, but because needs
were few and were easily met, the people had the opportunity
of turning to art, religion and other forms of culture. We already find in the first millennium a highly developed tradition
of sculpture in black marble which is associated with the Pala
kings of Bengal. Bengal's cotton fabrics had also established
their reputation as among the finest in the world.

The Pala kings were Hindu but they seem to have followed
the liberal and tolerant tradition prevalent since Asoka's time.
There was hardly any persecution of the Buddhists who constituted the majority of the people of Bengal. This happy
situation changed after the advent of the Sena kings. They
were ardent supporters of Brahminism and restored the pri-
macy of caste. A thousand years of Buddhism had so blurred
the distinctions of caste in Bengal that the Sena kings had to
import five Brahmin and five Kayastha families from upper
India to rebuild the hierarchy of caste. Those who clung to
Buddhism were given a low social status but even then Buddhism—openly in its south-east corner and in a debased or
disguised form in other areas—persisted in Bengal.

The attempt to restore Brahminism did not attain in Bengal
the success which it met in other parts of India. People in
general were sullen and resentful of this new imposition. Nor
did the Sena kings have enough time to re-establish Brahminism firmly. Before the restoration of caste could be complete,
the Sena dynasty was overthrown by the Pathans. Legend has
it that a handful of Pathan horsemen conquered Bengal. This
would have been impossible unless they found widespread
local support. What probably happened was a revolt of the
people against the ruling dynasty as soon as its power was
challenged by foreign invaders.

From the beginning of the thirteenth till the middle of the
eighteenth century, Bengal remained at first under Pathan
and later under Mughal domination. The rule was never complete or absolute. As in earlier days, the rulers were content to

collect taxes and extract general obedience. So long as their authority was not challenged the people were left to live their own lives. Many of the noblemen were Hindus. The collection of revenues was left largely in their hands. Rulers of Bengal in their turn owed allegiance to the Emperor of Delhi. This suzerainty was often even more nominal than the domination of the king over local nobles. During the Pathan days, the Sultans of Delhi were never really in control of the whole of India. The Mughals exercised greater central control but the governors still had large powers. There was little interference with the normal life of the people so long as allegiance to the emperor was not denied.

It may be said that the real development of Bengali as a language of literature and culture began with the Pathan rulers. Buddhism had encouraged the growth of literature in local languages and there are relics of early Bengali poetry which go back to the ninth century. Till the advent of the Muslims, Sanskrit was however the language of scholarship and culture. The Pathan kings had no special love for Sanskrit. In fact they may have felt that the dethronement of Sanskrit would help to break the domination of Brahminism. They also felt the need to stress their identity with the local people in their effort to resist the authority of Delhi. It was easier for them to understand the cultural background of their subjects through a living language like Bengali than a classical language like Sanskrit. By the middle of the fourteenth century the Pathan Sultans had established their political and cultural independence of Delhi. They encouraged translations of Sanskrit and Persian classics into Bengali partly as a political measure against attacks from Delhi, partly as an instrument to weaken the hold of the Brahmins and partly because of human considerations which inevitably grow when people live together. The upshot was that the Pathan kings became great patrons of Bengali literature.

This tradition of support for local literature was continued and in fact extended under the Mughals. The Pathan kings may have played a more direct role, but under the Mughals, patronage was offered by a much larger number of feudal nobles. Besides, the process of time resulted in a greater assimilation between the rulers and the ruled. The establishment of peace and the extension of markets led to increasing prosperity and encouraged a freer expression of the artistic spirit of the people. Another factor which helped was the enrichment of the cultural life of the people through the impact of Islam. The revival of Brahminism had not met with as great a success in Bengal as in the rest of India. The Buddhist tradition of egalitarianism resisted the attempt to impose a new hierarchy. With the advent of Muslim rulers, many who had accepted Brahminism under pressure, repudiated it and went over into the fold of Islam. It has often been noticed that there is a larger proportion of Muslims in north-western and north-eastern India than in the rest of the country. The concentration in the north-west is easy to understand. It is on the direct route by which the Muslims poured into India. The phenomenon in the north-east is more surprising and can be explained only if we remember that this region was the last stronghold of Buddhism in India and many of its adherents preferred Islam with its greater democratic appeal to orthodox Brahminism.

Be that as it may, the impact of Islam led to a further loosening of the bonds of caste and religious rituals in Bengal. There was in consequence an efflorescence of both secular and religious literature. The *Vaishnava* poets who flourished during this period have written some of the finest lyrics found in any language of the world. The outburst of devotional poetry was a general phenomenon throughout medieval India. We find wonderful specimens of lyric poetry in regions so far flung and separated as Bengal and Maharashtra, Oudh and Tamilnad. What was of special interest was the emergence in Bengal of a new type of secular poetry in ballads and folk tales. This again was largely due to the impact of Islam which had a more secular outlook than either Buddhism or Brahminism. The artistic spirit of the people found its main expression in literature but we may also mention the emergence of the muslin whose delicacy and fineness became legendary throughout the world. There were some monuments built by the Pathan and Mughal rulers but, by and large, sculpture and architecture did not reach any great height during this period.

Europeans started coming to Bengal towards the end of the sixteenth century. There are references to Portuguese, Dutch, French and British settlements in different parts of the province. As early as the beginning of the seventeenth century, Jehangir had the capital of Bengal shifted to Dacca in the east to check the depredations of Portuguese pirates. There are references to clashes with other European adventurers during the reign of Shahjahan. Till the middle of the eighteenth century, the Europeans were primarily traders depending on the favour and patronage of the Indian rulers. In 1757, the Battle of Plassey changed this, and the British became the dominant power in Bengal, Bihar and Orissa. In the course of the century, the British triumphed over all other European and Indian rivals. Calcutta became the capital of British possessions in India. It was from this centre that the subjugation of the Indian sub-continent was achieved. After the great Indian uprising of 1857, the British Crown assumed direct dominion over India.

The British Empire in India differed from the earlier Indian empires in several important ways. Perhaps the most important of these was the impact of the western world upon the people's way of life. Whatever their original intentions may have been, earlier invaders all finally became denizens of the land. They settled down and intermarried with the native population till in course of time they became as much Indian as the people they had dispossessed. This assimilation was made the easier because the invaders invariably came in small groups and communications were difficult. A handful of settlers who have lost contact with their original homeland cannot long retain their separate identity. The pre-British invaders of India were all in course of time lost in the sea of Indian humanity. The British on the other hand had no intention of settling in India. By choice, they remained mere birds of passage. There may have been individual exceptions, but by and large a policy of regular turnover of the British personnel was maintained. This ensured that each batch came for a stipulated period and was then recalled home while a fresh batch took its place. The British impact on India thus always remained that of an external force with its base many thousand miles away.

Paradoxically, this external influence has proved more far-reaching than the wholesale immigration of earlier invaders. The main reason for this is to be found in the industrial revolution which was transforming the European scene. Earlier invaders who had poured into India had also triumphed because of superior military or social organisation but the superiority was one of degree, not kind. Europe's entry into India coincided with the transformation of her economic, social and political life through the application of science to the production and distribution of goods. The new techniques of production and even more the growth of a new scientific outlook gave Europe a superiority that was not merely of degree but of kind. Faced with the competition of machine-made goods and mechanical transportation, India's old economy was completely disrupted. Her trade and industry decayed, her social forms disintegrated and even her religious beliefs were challenged. A process of ferment and dissolution began which is continuing to this day.

Another important difference was that the pre-British empires were land-based and, excepting the Mauryan Empire, their centres of power were in north-central or north-west India. Bengal had always been on the periphery of the former empires and generally the last area to come under and the first to break away from central control. In the case of the British Empire, the position was reversed. Bengal became for the first time the centre of all political, economic and cultural activities in India and was more deeply affected by the impact of the western influence than any other part of the country.

Calcutta remained the capital of British India till 1911. It was not only the political centre but also the industrial and cultural metropolis of India during this period. No doubt there were other important centres like Bombay and Madras, but the pre-eminence of Calcutta was beyond question. European influence permeated from this centre and profoundly affected the education, the social habits and to some extent even the religion of the people. Movements for religious and social reform became increasingly influenced by western ideals. Bombay and Madras were also centres of Europeanisation which generally meant modernisation. Nevertheless, the main centre of ferment and modernisation remained Calcutta. Some of these newly westernised Bengalis went to absurd lengths. There are stories of young Bengalis who flaunted their modernism by going about in the street with roast beef in their hands. There were others who took pride in the fact that they could hardly speak Bengali and wrote, thought and dreamt in English! It is not an accident that Raja Ram Mohan Roy, who has often been described as the father of Modern India, came from this region.

If British domination over the Indian sub-continent began in Calcutta, the attempts to overthrow that domination also began in the same city. As early as the first decade of the nineteenth century, Ram Mohan Roy talked of western education as a means of achieving self-government. He was perhaps the first, but soon there were others in Bengal who began to talk of liberty, equality and fraternity as political objectives to be realised by the Indian people. The earliest rumblings of the great uprising of 1857 were heard in Barrackpur, fourteen miles from Calcutta. Murshidabad which had been the capital of the Mughals was another centre of discontent and political ferment. The first session of the Indian National Congress was held in Bombay, but its President was W. C. Bonnerjee, a leading lawyer from Calcutta. Agitation for Home Rule found one of its strongest centres in this city. In the first decade of the twentieth century, the movement for direct action and boycott of British goods began in Bengal. The partition of Bengal in 1905 has been described as the beginning of mass political agitation in India. The annulment of that partition in 1912 was the first great success of the Indian nationalist movement. Terrorism as a political instrument also appeared first in this part of India. In fact, till the emergence of Mahatma Gandhi in the twenties of the present century, political leadership in the Indian sub-continent was, by and large, supplied by the intellectuals of Bengal.

II

F R O M the beginning of her history, Bengal has been predominantly an agricultural land. The land is alluvial and built up by immense masses of loam, clay and sand brought down by the Ganges and the Brahmaputra in their long march to the sea. With innumerable rivers and canals crossing one another in intricate patterns, the soil is fertile and yields rich harvests of rice with a minimum of effort. With so much water all around and fish as plentiful as the lush green grass in the monsoon months, it is not surprising that people should by and large be fish eaters. In fact, rice and fish may well be regarded as the staple food of the people.

In theory, Bengal has six seasons but only four are well marked. Summer begins in February and continues to mid-June. The sky is bare of clouds and a tropical sun shines with cruel intensity. The afternoons are hot and at times sultry, with wild winds raking up dust and dead leaves. Even then the heat is never so severe as in the northern parts of India. The monsoons bring welcome relief. One of the most beautiful sights of the year is the approach of rain-laden clouds in early June. The parched earth is soaked with rain and vegetation bursts forth in tropical abundance. By the middle of September, the monsoons are over and autumn sets in. The clouds do not yet disappear but they are light and fleecy and float lazily across the blue rain-washed sky. Sun and shower follow in quick succession and there are sunsets of unbelievable splendour. Then comes a short spell of winter from November to February. The air is cool with occasionally a touch of chill in the early morning hours, but it is never really cold. The pleasant winter merges into summer almost before one realises that spring has slipped past with light uncertain steps.

Bengal is flat except in the north where it rises into the foothills of the Himalayas. To the east and the west lie low hills which divide it from Assam and Bihar. In between lies a vast alluvial plain dotted with clusters of villages. When one flies over Bengal, the impression is of a vast green carpet intersected by innumerable channels of silver water and marked by groves of dark green trees which hide the villages. Though there are occasional gusts of fury and storm, nature is on the whole gentle and kind. So are the people. Even if they are roused to quick excitement, their temper subsides easily and leaves them a placid, mild-mannered and friendly folk.

The majority of the people of Bengal have lived and still live in villages. Till recent decades, agriculture, fishing and weaving have been the common callings. Villages have been largely self-sufficient and lived their own lives, undisturbed by what happened outside. The houses are clustered together while the fields belonging to the villagers are spread all around. Different castes or communities generally live in different sections of the village but there has always been freedom of movement and social intercourse. Regardless of differences in caste and religion, the village community has felt and acted as one.

In an agricultural community which has depended mainly on the monsoons for its water supply, work in the fields has been seasonal. During the busy months, men and boys stream out of the village in the early hours of the morning and return late in the afternoon. Short bursts of intense activity are followed by long periods when there is little to do except watch nature pursue her own steady course for ripening the harvest. In fact, for about four months in the year villagers have little to do and cannot even move about freely as large parts of the

country are inundated with water. With so much time on their
hands, it is not surprising that even the average villager turns
to thoughts about life, death and destiny. The dependence on
nature for the success of the harvest gives further strength to
such musings. From the earliest times, the villagers of Bengal
have built their festivals and religious rites on a sense of sub-
mission to destiny.

Where men find the means of survival easily, they turn
readily to philosophy, religion and art. Bengal is another
example of this universal human tendency. Even the poorest
houses in the villages are usually clean and tidy and adorned
by a few expressions of simple art. The women dress simply but
not without artistic effect. Village swains take a great deal of
care in personal adornment. Youths with glossy locks carefully
dressed in long curls are quite a common sight. The normal
household duties are performed like an elaborate ritual. The
women of Bengal spend perhaps more time in cooking than
those in other parts of India. Special mention may be made of
the Harvest Dinners held in early November and the Festival
of Cakes celebrated in the middle of January. The Harvest
Dinner is comparable to the American Thanksgiving Day while
the Festival of Cakes is a day on which the housewife really
lets herself go in preparing all kinds of sweets and cakes for the
family and neighbours. Women start preparing for these days
weeks ahead and take great pride in making special types of
food and sweets. Bengali women are also famous for their skill
in decorating their houses with patterns of great intricacy and
beauty. Called *alpanas*, these patterns may be drawn in lime,
chalk, powdered rice or any other material which stands out
clearly against the dull brown earth. These *alpanas* are also
drawn on pots and pitchers and sometimes on doors and walls.
On special occasions, they are carefully painted before the door
to welcome the in-coming guest.

Life has continually become harder since the beginning of
the present century and this has considerably reduced the joy
of life among the village people. In spite of this, a casual visitor

to Bengal will be struck by the music which seems to be a part
of the life of the people in the villages. In the western areas,
shepherd boys lead their herds to graze and play on their flutes
as they sit in the shade under hot summer skies. Farmers sing
as they go out in the morning or return in the evening. In the
eastern parts, fishermen's songs are invariably an accompani-
ment to their work. In the autumn, the winds are steady and
boats move across the water with hoisted sails. Relieved of the
task of rowing, the boatmen give themselves to singing songs
of joy and sorrow, of life and death, of fate and destiny. It is
an unforgettable experience to see the sun shine on sails of
many colours and hear the music wafted across the silent
waters.

In the past there was community singing almost every evening during the harvest season. The tradition has not yet died.
Even today, after the harvest is gathered and the mild winter
sets in, there are religious festivals and plays. Many of these
are based on the myths and legends that have grown out of the
Ramayana and the *Mahabharata*. Side by side with such plays
and recitations, there is also a body of folk literature based on
the traditions of Muslim heroes and saints. People of one community have always attended the festivals and plays of the
other and participated in a common cultural life.

The wandering minstrel is found in other parts of India as
well, but nowhere else is there so strong a religious movement
based on song and music. The *bauls*, the *dervishes* and the *kir-
tanias* are in a sense peculiar to Bengal. They sing of the highest
thoughts in simple words. Truths of the *Upanishads* as well as
the insights of the Sufi mystics are translated into terms which
the common villager can understand. It is notable that many
of these songs use agricultural practices and customs to describe some of the highest mystic experiences of man. The
kirtan in particular is typical of Bengal. The songs are inspired
by utter abandonment and surrender. Emotions rise to an
unbearable intensity, but even in moments of the most intense
passion, the sense of community with the life of the soil is not

lost. In the midst of total surrender and identification with the Absolute, little incidents common to rural life are brought in to establish the kinship between ordinary and mystic experiences.

Till the beginning of the present century, life in Bengal has been predominantly rural. There have no doubt been some large towns besides the capital, but their existence did not in any way disturb the dominantly rural temper of the people. As in agricultural communities all over the world, people were friendly, hospitable and somewhat rustic. It has often been said that Bengalis are sincere and hearty but do not know courtly manners. This lack of polish in ordinary social inter-course has not prevented the growth of warm friendship be-tween men of different communities. It is only in the last three or four decades that the rural temper has changed and the urban population taken a larger share in determining the pat-tern of social life.

In an agricultural community, the majority of the people are poor and live near the subsistence level. Bengal is no ex-ception. The majority of her villagers have always led and still lead a hard and strenuous life. Where people live near the margin, it is inevitable that a certain harshness and poverty of the spirit should develop. Villagers in Bengal have to some extent escaped this consequence of privation and want because of one peculiar feature in the social structure. This is the pre-sence of an inordinately large number of gradations in the social hierarchy. As in most patriarchal societies, each higher social stratum has adopted a somewhat paternal attitude to-wards the lower strata. The multiplicity of such strata in Bengal has in the past led to a closer and more human relationship than in areas where the differences between such strata are too great.

During the days of Pathan and Mughal rule, Bengal had a large number of noblemen who were independent in fact, even if not in name. Unlike other parts of India, Bengal rarely enjoyed central rule. The king owed only a nominal allegiance to the Emperor of Delhi and the local noblemen were equally lax in their attitude to the king. Both the kings and the nobles repudiated higher authority at the first signs of weakness above. The result was the growth of a large number of centres of local power instead of one princely court. This may have hindered political consolidation and perhaps retarded economic development, but its effect on the development of art and literature was beneficial. Poets and literary men could easily find patronage and the competition among the noblemen offered greater opportunities to men of letters.

During the last two hundred years or so, the expansion of a comparatively well-to-do class became more marked. The establishment of the capital in Calcutta created many opportunities for acquiring wealth and power. The consolidation of the land tenure and the establishment of the Permanent Settlement led to the creation of a landed aristocracy with many levels of subsidiary landlords and tenants. This has led to a disproportionate increase in the size of what may be called a middle class. At least since the end of the eighteenth century, there has been in Bengal a multiplicity of intermediaries between the cultivator and the state. They have not generally worked with their hands and in many cases their connection with the land has been remote. Many of them have belonged to the class of absentee landlords. As in other countries of the world, the system has led to indolence, corruption and sapping of initiative. Economists, political theorists and social philosophers have condemned the system in no uncertain terms. Nevertheless it has had one redeeming feature in encouraging the growth of art and literature. The expansion of a class of people who were above want and could devote their leisure to the pursuit of literature is one major reason for the literary renaissance which swept over Bengal in the nineteenth century.

The growth of towns has greatly changed the tenor of the people's life. Metropolitan cities are the same all over the world —huge, impersonal and perhaps a little heartless but full of a restless, seething energy. Small towns seek to emulate the

metropolis but cannot break away from the hold of the countryside. Their life is dominated by the lower middle classes and
reflects their concern to preserve gentility on an income which
is hardly adequate for bare sustenance. Small towns are thus
full of people who are restless, ambitious and slightly embit-
tered. The unsuccessful lawyer, the petty official and the hard-
pressed clerk very often set the pattern of social life in the small
town. There is a veneer of respectability but below seethe the
frustrations, passions and fears of a class that is never sure of
itself.

The farmer in the village is more rooted in his traditional
life. He is poor and often lacks the necessities of life. In the
present day world, he also is often discontented. One of the
major changes which have taken place in the last hundred
years or so is the growth of discontent in the countryside. In
earlier days, the peasant's attitude was one of acquiescence if
not acceptance of his fate. He may have occasionally grumbled
but the grumbling itself was half-hearted. He knew his status
in society and accepted it for what it was worth. This gave him
a dignity which even his social superiors often lacked. It also
gave him a philosophy which sought to compensate the hardships of the present life by the promise of better days in a world
hereafter or in succeeding lives.

While the economy and agriculture of Bengal has on the
whole been dominated by men, it would be a mistake to forget
the role that women have played. Artistic decorations in
households have been primarily their work. They have evolved
their own forms of religious rites and festivals. While the men
have developed their own brand of community singing, the
women have not lagged behind. They have special festivals
centred round family life which are partly religious and partly
social. They have also their own special forms of religious duties
and observances. Grouped under the generic name of *Vrata* or
vow, many of these begin in early childhood. There is a
special rite which a young girl performs to secure a good
husband when she grows up. There are other rites specially

devoted to the welfare of the husband and children. Still others relate to the prosperity of the family. With growing urbanisation and spread of education, many of these customs and rites are disappearing but the woman is still regarded as the centre of the home. Family welfare is her special charge. In former days there were of course no women's clubs or societies in the modern sense, but like women elsewhere in the world, women in Bengal found ways of gathering together for women's talk. Often they gathered round the well or met together in the afternoon when the day's work was done to gossip about current events. Sometimes these gatherings had a religious character and stories from the scriptures were read or discussed.

A brief description of the normal life of a village woman may give the foreign reader a more vivid sense of what life still is in the villages of Bengal. The housewife is generally the first to wake up in the morning. This will be while it is still dark in both summer and winter months. For many, an early morning dip in the neighbouring river or tank will mark the beginning of the day even during the winter. Then start preparations for the morning. Breakfast for the children and the men must be ready before they go out to work. In olden days this would be puffed rice or perhaps some of the rice and fish left over from the previous night. Nowadays, it is not unusual for a farmer to demand a cup of tea even in the villages. By seven or seven-thirty, the men move out to work and the woman sets about her household duties. In the past she had to husk the paddy to get rice for the mid-day meal. She also has to collect and chop vegetables and cook the meal. Hundreds of other odds and ends make up the toll of her domestic duties. When the food is ready, she has to carry it to the fields during the busy season. The men have no time to come home for their meals. Then she returns and has her own meal and perhaps rests for a little while. There will then be an hour or two's break before her evening chores begin. This interval is the time for rest, recreation and gossip. Women collect in a friendly house and talk while they sew or mend clothes.

A special type of art which developed out of these women's gatherings was the *kantha* or patchwork quilt made of odd bits of cloth. A careful housewife throws hardly anything away. Strips from her own *saris* or from her husband's *dhotis* as well as bits of cloth from *banians* or shirts are put together and sewn till a cotton quilt is ready. This is then embroidered and the fame of the housewife depends upon the skill of her embroidery. There are some remarkable specimens of *kanthas* which depict not only village scenes but also bring out vividly stories from the scriptures or the epics.

Evening sees another round of busy household activities. Food has again to be prepared for the men back from work. Normally all meals are over either by sunset or immediately thereafter. The men sit round with a *hooka*, an Indian pipe, and exchange views about men and matters. Sometimes they meet in the village school or at the mosque or the temple. Women busy themselves with putting the children to bed and performing their religious rites. Lighting the evening lamp is an elaborate ritual and part of the inescapable duty of every village woman. By eight-thirty or nine, everything becomes quiet and the village goes to sleep. Year in and year out, the same routine is followed with hardly any variation. The only break in the monotony of life comes when there is a marriage, a birth or a death or when some daring or foolish man or woman breaks away from traditional things.

III

To the world outside, Bengali literature means almost exclusively the work of Rabindranath Tagore. This is not surprising because it was the genius of Tagore which lifted a language of an Indian province to the status of a world language. Tagore is the greatest poet, short-story writer, essayist and composer of Bengal and one of the greatest the world has known. He is also among the greatest of Bengal's novelists and dramatists, though in these fields he may not rank among the world's masters. His work stretches over a period of more than sixty years and covers almost every phase in the modern development of Bengal's language and literature.

His pre-eminence cannot be questioned but it would be wrong to think that he exhausts the infinite capacity of the language and literature of Bengal. In the field of poetry, we have distinguished names like those of Chandidas, Vidyapati, Alawal, Kritiibas, Daulat Kazi, Kasiramdas, Mukunda Ram, Bharat Chandra, Ramprasad and Michael Madhusudan Dutt. The Vaishnava poets were supreme lyricists. Chandidas in particular attained an utter simplicity and abandon which has rarely been equalled. He is believed to have flourished in the fifteenth century but the language he used is timeless as it welled out of the depths of the people's experience. It has a clarity which makes his poems seem contemporaneous with the most modern poets of Bengal. Vidyapati, who was a near contemporary, lived in the borderland between Bengal and Bihar and is claimed by the two sister languages of Bengali and Hindi. The great Sanskrit epics, the *Ramayana* and the *Mahabharata*, were translated under the direct patronage of the Pathan kings of Bengal. It is also of interest to note that among the earlier poets of Bengal were many Moslems. Two of them, Alawal and Daulat Kazi have already been mentioned. Alawal wrote a highly Sanskritised language but the script he used was Arabic. Daulat Kazi had perhaps even greater promise but died comparatively young.

The Vaishnava lyrics were the spontaneous expression of individual poets. The programmes of translation were carried out under court patronage. Of still greater interest is the development in medieval Bengal of a great body of poetry which may be called the literature of folk religions. These poems sing of obscure deities who had no place in the regular Hindu pantheon. Suggestions have been made that they were either tribal gods or goddesses, or perhaps some of the divinities which had found a place in corrupt Buddhism. The main

interest of the poems lies in the vivid picture they give of the
life of the ordinary people. They purport to sing of gods and
goddesses but often the god is nothing but a prosperous farmer
while the goddess is indistinguishable from the devoted housewife of Bengal. At other times, the god or goddess is cast in the
image of a local tyrant. One may hazard the guess that the poet
at times gave vent to his resentment against a local ruler in
this fashion. Many of these poems describe the seasons in great
detail and also give a complete picture of the domestic life, the
social activities and the normal pursuits of the people at large.

From the folk religious poetry to the frankly secular poem is
but one short step. In the ballads of Mymensingh and Sylhet
we find beautiful tales in verse which speak of the joys and
sorrows of common folk. The common man has found an
honoured place in literature only in recent times. Formerly,
poetry and drama and even stories concerned themselves
mainly with the doings of gods and goddesses, kings and queens
and the upper classes in society. If an ordinary citizen was
brought in, it was often to serve as an object of ridicule or a
foil for the activities of the more privileged groups. It is therefore surprising that, so early as the sixteenth or seventeenth
century. Bengal should have produced poetry instinct with
such a democratic spirit.

It is also interesting to note that in the poetry of folk religion
as well as in the secular poetry of the day, there are many
references to the adventures of merchants, princes and sailors
in lands across the seas. A mercantile community is generally
less hierarchical than a society based on the possession of land.
This may have been one of the factors responsible for the
early emergence of a more democratic temper in Bengali
literature. The deeper force at work was of course the long
tradition of social democracy initiated by Buddhism and later
strengthened by the impact of Islam.

The progress of Bengali literature began in the Middle Ages
under the patronage of Pathan kings. The first great poet of
modern Bengal was a Christian. Michael Madhusudan Dutt

was not only a great Bengali lyricist but also the first epic poet
of modern India. The history of his life is in some ways an
interesting comment on the changes which were taking place
in the country. He began with an utter contempt for everything
Indian. He studied English as well as some other ancient and
modern European languages and did everything he could to
turn himself into a European. His conversion to Christianity
was due not so much to his belief in Christ as to his desire to
identify himself with Europe. His wife was British and his first
poems were written in English. Soon he realised that if he was
to make any permanent contribution to literature he must
turn to his native language. Once this became clear to him, he
turned all his energy and genius to the enrichment of Bengali.
He is Bengal's first epic poet, dramatist, sonneteer and satirist.

Michael Madhusudan Dutt's poetry is full of revolt and
tumult. Whether he reacted against the ancient traditions of
India or later against some of the customs and beliefs borrowed
from modern Europe, his writing is marked by a rare intellectual energy and passion characteristic of a new birth. In Tagore,
this renaissance is stabilised. He accepted the traditions of
ancient and medieval India without any mental reservation
and enriched them by his easy acceptance of the heritage of
the western world. There is a fullness in his writings which at
times merges into a tinge of sadness and melancholy. One of
the supreme lyric poets of the world, his work has been translated into almost all languages of the world. Nevertheless, he
has been only partially presented to those who do not know
Bengali. The translations have been confined to poems of one
type and do not reflect the variety, the massiveness and the
masculine vigour of his intellect and imagination. To give one
example : Those who have read Tagore only in translation will
be surprised to hear that he was one of the chief spokesmen
of the people during the political struggle of 1905. His songs
and speeches inspired the people then and still have an appeal
for not only his own countrymen but for men and women of
generous instincts anywhere in the world. The secret of their

permanent interest lies in Tagore's positive outlook. In all his
numerous writings, there is hardly a word of bitterness or
hatred against the British. He realised that freedom meant not
the mere removal of British rule but the development of the
people's personality in all spheres of human activity. He therefore spoke of creative self-expression for the individual and the
community in a context of understanding and sympathy among
the nations of the world.

Among Tagore's successors there may be none who has his
supreme genius but the variety and vitality of Bengali poetry
in the last fifty years would bear comparison with almost any
literature of the world. Sentiment and feeling, social problems
and controversy, satire and intellectuality have all contributed
in different degrees to give a distinctive tone to much of contemporary writing which marks it from the poetry of Tagore.
There have been conscious propagandists who have preached
nationalism or patriotism, socialism or communism or indivi-
dualism of diverse types. Others have sought refuge from the
hard facts of life in an ivory tower of imagery and symbolism.
Others still have gone back to prehistoric times and found in
anthropology and myth sustenance for their imaginations and
their hopes.

One of the most interesting examples of how these new forces
have worked is found in the poetry of Kazi Nazrul Islam. Just
as Tagore was the poet of the Swadeshi Movement of 1905,
Nazrul Islam may be described as the poet of the national
struggle in the thirties of this century. Earlier, he had reflected
the turmoil created by the impact of the Russian Revolution
and written a series of poems and songs which breathe un-
compromising opposition to tyranny and injustice in every
form. In spite of the many blemishes in his writings—imma-
turity, bombast and rhetoric and occasionally even lapses in
taste—he has been hailed as a people's poet *par excellence*.

The other contemporary poets may be divided among those
who have generally conformed to the tradition of Tagore and
those who have sought to strike out new paths of their own.

These rebels have often sought to derive inspiration from and establish their affiliation with present-day western poets in their bitterness and disdain for the sorry state of things in the modern world. In place of Tagore's serenity, their poems are full of unrest and cynicism. His sense of unity is replaced in the younger poets with the consciousness of the broken fragments of life. The lyric note gives place to satire, irony or a sense of frustration, despair and disgust. In some, these new elements have tended to crowd out the authentic note of poetry but, among the best poets, there has often been a successful fusion of imaginative and intellectual qualities. There have also been poets who surrendered themselves to the mood of the moment and allowed a flood of sensations to carry them along. In a word, variety and experiment are the characteristic note of many contemporary Bengali poets as will be seen in the poems which follow.

IV

T H E story-teller's is one of the most ancient arts in history. In earlier times, except for tales of wit and humour or those meant for children, stories generally centred round some religious or moral theme. There were also stories of heroic or amorous adventures of kings or princes, but almost all of them lacked verisimilitude and truth of nature. It perhaps needed a more self-conscious and sophisticated society to develop the story in the modern sense. It is therefore somewhat surprising to find that secular stories first appeared in Bengal during the Middle Ages. Some of the ballads and tales in rhyme which flourished in Mymensingh and Sylhet may be regarded as the precursors of the story in Bengali literature.

Nevertheless they were only precursors and the modern story in the proper sense appears in the nineteenth century. There were translations from Sanskrit and Persian tales even in the Middle Ages but it is the impact of European literature that led to the development of the Bengali short story. The most important characteristic of this new development is the emphasis on character as opposed to reportage. Stories in earlier days, and this applies as much to western as to eastern countries, had dealt mainly with events. Their interest centred round the plot and hardly any attention was paid to character or individuality. By the middle of the eighteenth century the situation had changed in Europe and the novel and the short story emerged as distinct forms of art. Bengali was the first Indian literature to be influenced by this western development.

Bankim Chandra Chatterjee has been acknowledged as the first novelist and short-story writer of Bengal in the modern period. Like Michael Madhusudan Dutt, his first work was also in English but he quickly realised that he must write in Bengali if he was to make any real contribution to literature. There is little doubt that he was deeply influenced by Sir Walter Scott. His earlier novels deal with historical themes and the atmosphere reminds one strongly of Scott. In some of his later novels, he deals with contemporary social problems. He had a vivid imagination but he lacks the power to create the atmosphere of a bygone age. His novels dealing with the life of men and women of his own times have therefore a greater vitality, though even in these he often allows his moral predilections to interfere with his artistic values. It is not surprising that most critics have held that his social novels mark the highest development of his art.

Bankim Chandra Chatterjee was also the first short-story writer of note in modern Bengal. His short stories are in effect condensed novels. He made no attempt to develop the short story as a distinct and unique form of art. If one attempts to differentiate between these two forms, one may say that the novel deals with growth of character and is a world complete in itself. The short story on the other hand deals with a situation or aspect of character that is piquant and excites the curiosity or imagination of the artist. Short stories are vignettes of life rather than a reflection of life in its totality. They may thus in one sense be likened to lyric poems. Chatterjee's stories however lack this lyric note.

There were a host of writers who followed Bankim Chandra Chatterjee. Most of them tried their hand at both novels and short stories. The novels were often historical but social novels dealing with contemporary events gradually became more numerous. In the case of the short story also, most of these writers followed Chatterjee and stressed plot rather than the development of character.

Rabindranath Tagore is the first writer of Bengal who fully satisfies the requirements of the modern short story. He is not only a pioneer but also a supreme master in this field. In the Greek legend, Pallas Athene is supposed to have been born full grown from the head of Zeus. This certainly seems to hold true in the field of art. Very often, the first writer is also the greatest. Tagore has described his short stories as the life of Bengal seen through the window of his moving boat. Since the view is only from a window, there is no attempt at completeness or totality. Since the boat is moving, characters and events are seen for a fleeting moment. The partial and momentary visions however surprise us by their truth and insight. There is no attempt at expressing any definite philosophy of life, but no artist can help revealing something of himself in his art. What is more surprising is the understanding and sympathy which enables Tagore to light up segments of the people's life.

Bengal was fortunate in having as the immediate successors of Tagore several story writers of high quality. Prabhat Kumar Mukherjee first made his name with stories about the experience of Indian students abroad. These young men left home and country at a most impressionable age. It was a period in their lives when they longed for affection and sympathy. Romance also called to them and it was not surprising that many of them would become emotionally entangled during their foreign sojourn. Mukherjee captures their mood of hope and expectancy and their sense of loyalty to two different worlds. It is not surprising that there should be a note of nostalgia in much of his writing, but later he exhibited unsuspected powers of humour and irony. He wrote about the middle classes and has depicted many of their faults and foibles with keen insight and imaginative sympathy.

Sarat Chandra Chatterjee has a much bigger canvas. Many people regard him, and not without justification, as the most successful novelist of Bengal and perhaps of modern India. His sympathy was with the oppressed, the outcaste and the rejected of society. He wrote of naughty boys and perverse men and women. He brought into the Bengali story the life and experience of the fallen woman. He had travelled extensively and suffered deeply. He had shared the life of hardship and poverty which is the lot of almost all who deviate from the beaten path. His sympathy was with them, for his general attitude was that they are more sinned against than sinning. His imaginative identification with the waifs and strays of life at times shocked the conventional writers. There is no doubt that there was in him an element of the rebel who challenged accepted beliefs and customs. He is not so rich in creative imagination, his interests are not sufficiently wide and he is often carried away by sentimentalism, but these defects are overcome by his deep sympathy with human suffering and his faith in the innate dignity of man. With all his shortcomings, Chatterjee's stories are of the earth, earthy. They are born of the soil of Bengal: moist, humid and warm. Chatterjee struck an immediate chord in the sentiment of the Bengali people. From the publication of his first story, he became the idol of the Bengali and in course of time of the Indian public.

Both Prabhat Kumar Mukherjee and Sarat Chandra Chatterjee were deeply influenced by Tagore but each brought into the Bengali story a distinctive timbre of his own. Pramatha Chaudhury and Rajsekhar Bose brought a new note of irony and sophistication. Chaudhury had a light and gentle touch in which intellect was the guiding principle. He was deeply influenced by the French spirit and much of his writing has the quality of Gallic wit. Bose laughs equally at ancient superstitions and modern prejudices. He has a keen eye for the odd and bizarre and develops his irony out of the situation in which he places his characters.

In the beginning, the dominant influence on the Bengali story had been the English novel. By the end of the nineteenth century, French influence was becoming perceptible. Many of the stories of Pramatha Chaudhury have an ironic quality and lightness of touch that reminds one of the French masters. There were not only many translations of Maupassant but for some decades his influence was almost supreme. From the beginning of the present century, a new influence which made itself felt was that of the Russian masters, Tolstoy, Dostoevsky and Turgeniev became the models for many of the best writers of the day. There is a kinship between the brooding, mystic and introverted mentalities of the Russian and the Bengali writers. Temperament is one of the most important characteristics of the Russian novel and short story. Temperament is equally a dominant feature of many of the Bengali short stories written in the early decades of the present century.

From the twenties of the present century, the continental influence has been increasing in strength. After the Russian phase came the impact of Scandinavian literature. Sweden and Norway for a while dominated the mind of literary Bengal. In course of time the influence of German, Italian, Spanish and in very recent years that of American literature have also been increasingly felt.

Reference should be made to two new influences which have made a deep mark on most contemporary writing in Bengal. Freud opened out a new region which till then had been only dimly known. For a while, it became the rage to delve into the unconscious and the subconscious to look for new subjects and themes. The thirties of the present century saw the influence of Freud equalled and in some cases surpassed by that of Marx. Story writers and novelists often took up the role of social and political reformers with a self-conscious pose. Much of the new writing was ephemeral and many writers who achieved a quick

fame have been equally quickly forgotten. Nevertheless, there
is no denying that the impact of Freud and Marx led to a
deepening of sympathies and imagination among all writers.
All these impacts from abroad have led to a broadening of the
scope of the short story. Today, short stories may deal with
political or social problems or may be mere expressions of a
lyric spirit. They may also be a cross-section or moment in the
stream of consciousness. Not only has the attitude, mood and
treatment changed but the subject matter today is drawn from
all sections of society. It is no longer merely the upper or the
middle classes or the rejected of society who find a place in the
story. Uniqueness is sought not in the selection of the character
but in the way he or she is presented to the reader. Any person
from any walk of life may supply the theme of the story writer
in modern Bengal.

V

T H E present volume of poems and short stories does not
include anything from any of the past masters of Bengali
literature. It consists only of the work of writers who have
made their mark in the last quarter of a century. If it is asked
why earlier writers have thus been excluded, an answer may
be given on the following lines. The advent of the British set
in motion a process of disintegration of old Indian customs,
beliefs and institutions. This process has perhaps gone further
in Bengal than any other part of India. Its old agricultural
economy is slowly but inexorably giving place to one in which
industry is becoming the dominant force. Growing industrial-
isation accompanied by improvement in the means of commu-
nication has greatly increased the mobility of the people and
led to a steady drift of the population to the towns. The village
has become almost moribund and rural forms of life are decay-
ing at an accelerated rate. Institutions like the joint family are
breaking up. The disruption of the old economy has resulted in
widespread poverty, though a small proportion of the people

has become richer than before. European science has shaken the foundations of traditional Indian beliefs.

All the forces have combined to create a sense of uncertainty and unrest. There has been for some decades a sense of loss of direction and purpose among the younger generations. As education has spread, the number of educated unemployed has increased. As industries have developed, more and more people have been cast adrift from the moorings of rural life. Life has become harder in both village and town, and the lower middle classes, who form the backbone of Bengal's social structure, have become dispirited, frustrated and bitter. The break-up of the old order was becoming clear even before the outbreak of the World War in 1939. The war accelerated the process and changes began to gather a terrifying momentum after the entry of Japan in the war in 1941. This brought the conflict to Bengal's doorsteps. Instead of a backwater far removed from the scene of struggle, the province became a battlefront. Nor was there any release of enthusiasm and patriotic passion which enabled many other countries of the world to rise above the horrors of war. The tragedy of the Bengal Famine of 1943 was evidence of how low the spirit of the people had sunk. In 1946 came the great Calcutta killing and marked perhaps the nadir of this mood of despair and loss of all sense of values.

The attainment of independence in 1947 might have given a new purpose and sense of direction to the people but for the unfortunate fact of the partition of Bengal. In a sense, the partition of the province was even more tragic than the division of the sub-continent into India and Pakistan. The divided and distracted people have not yet felt the full glow of freedom and the continuing migration of the minority from East to West Bengal is preventing a consolidation of the undoubted progress which West Bengal has achieved. Nevertheless one feels the stirrings of a new life and the literature of the day reflects both the anxiety and disillusion, the fear and the uncertainties of the past as well as the glimmerings of hope in a brighter future.

The foreign reader will now appreciate why there has been a deliberate exclusion of earlier writers from this anthology. It is on the one hand intended to show that there is a wealth of talent in contemporary Bengal which makes its literature worthy of the attention of readers in other parts of the world. On the other, it is the purpose of this selection to give the world outside an insight into the mind of contemporary Bengal. It is natural to expect that these comparatively younger writers will reflect the present temper of the country more faithfully than earlier masters who passed their formative years in an era when Indian life still conformed to ancient patterns. Modern India presents the paradox of a mood in which rebellion and faith are almost equally strong and Bengal reflects that mood in its acutest form. Readers in other countries may find in these stories and poems a reflection of this questioning and brooding spirit which is driving resurgent India to attempt in literature and in life a new synthesis of ancient traditions and modern values.

22 *August* 1956   HUMAYUN KABIR

Green and Gold

One of Those

I

T H E train was steaming ahead into the dark night and Chandrababu was alone in the compartment.

There was none else around him, yet he was surrounded by heaps of mute mutterings. Around him lay scattered the feelings and thoughts of countless people—expressed in different languages and set down in diverse modes on different bits of paper. Silent yet curiously articulate.

A thin rain was beating down into the deep, dark night. This is the time of dreams, of flights on the wings of fancy. Chandrababu's eyes grew heavy at the thought. He put a *pan* [betel-leaf] into his mouth, took out a small box from his pocket and after tapping it caressingly, took a pinch of *jarda* [scented tobacco] to ginger up the chewed *pan*. He opened the window, spat out, and went on chewing. A strong wind was lashing against the train, and the window had to be closed. Chandrababu went back to his seat with slow steps. He hated unnecessary haste and youthful gusto. By nature, he was restful and deliberate.

He had already set apart the five letters he had chosen for the night. Were there more time, he would certainly have read many more. Such pursuits never tired his curious mind. He had carefully learned the various devices for opening letters without leaving any tell-tale marks and kept the necessary implements handy.

He ran his fingers over the envelopes before opening them. And then into the land of delicious dreams !

II

CHANDRABABU is not young, nor has he reached the
ineffective immobility of old age.   In fact, in outward seeming,
he is like a ripe and hardened coconut in human form.   He
is in declining middle age, but it is difficult to measure his
exact progress in this slow decline.   According to an entry
in his service record, he is forty-eight ; but that is a false
statement.   One does not know how many years he has saved
through this lie, for those who knew the truth are now all
dead.   Nor can one guess from his appearance ; he started
dyeing his hair as soon as he spotted some patches of grey.
He would not face any avoidable embarrassment in the presence
of Madhuri : she is his young third wife.

Whatever be his age, Chandrababu is something of an
aesthete.   The hard crust of the ripe coconut conceals a
soft kernel ; the apparent lack of animation in his glassy
eyes belies his dreamy nature.   Since adolescence, he has
pursued what he has considered the essence of experience.
He has never taken to writing poetry ; that has seemed
somewhat unsatisfying.   The main thing is to make poetry,
or, better still, to live it—to find the essence in *actual* experience.   That he has done throughout his life.   If his cousin
Tena were alive, he could have told with what eagerness in
his boyhood Chandrababu used to stand eavesdropping
outside the bedrooms of newly married couples.   How often
in those early days he listened behind open windows and looked
through peep-holes !   In his youth, he pursued such experiences
with greater vigour.   The history of that period was known
to his doctors of those days and his two earlier wives, both
of whom are long dead.   And by God's grace, he has found
a job peculiarly suited to his tastes.   He is a sorter in the
Postal Mail Van.

What varied experience he has gained from the letters
that have passed through his hands ! Occasionally, a letter-
head carries the name of a scholar of much distinction, a man

with an impressive array of academic degrees, but what filthy language he uses in writing to his wife (God knows if it is his wife)! Such unspeakable obscenity! But it is a pleasure to read.

In the early days, Chandrababu usually seized upon envelopes bearing addresses written in a feminine hand, but from long experience he has now learned that such letters are comparatively drab. The epistolary fare provided by women is mostly full of such banalities as, " I am well. How are you ?" At best one would find " My heart longs for you. When will you come ?"—and that inevitable " Please write to me. With the most respectful greetings............ " Occasionally, Chandrababu has been rewarded by one or two purple patches like " Take my kisses."

Perhaps once in a while, on a rare occasion, a woman's letter provides a real treat, but usually it is full of requests for things to be brought home—almost like a shopping list. On the whole, Chandrababu is sadly convinced of the epistolary deficiency of the female species.

But an envelope bearing the name and address of a woman, written in a man's hand, gives him a thrill. Not that even these have not sometimes disappointed him ; there are letters written in languages other than Bengali and English, letters from sons to mothers, and—the most annoying of all—letters addressed to women whose relationship with the writers remains curiously uncertain. But these are exceptions ; speaking generally, it is letters from men that hold the promise of bliss. Chandrababu has copied out some of the choicest extracts. Men are shameless—they can write without any inhibitions. Besides, they would take the wildest risks. Once he found a hundred-rupee note hidden in a letter. Photographs have been, of course, more frequent finds ; he has filled a private album with them. And what wonderful pictures ! —people of so many different races—how amazingly different were the poses—such breathtaking variety !

But one must not altogether reject the possibilities of the

feminine variety ; once a letter bore the full impress of a woman's lips.

III

T H E first letter Chandrababu opened was from a woman. But, as he had feared, it was disappointing. Still, he carefully went through it.

M Y D E A R S I S T E R ,

I received your letter yesterday. You use reply-paid post cards while writing to us. You should realise that this makes us feel embarrassed. You should also remember that here I am alone to carry the entire burden of the family. On top of it, I have my teaching job. There's not a moment's rest. However, I sent Gadadhar to the goldsmith a couple of days ago; your ornaments were ready. Last week, when I went myself, only the earrings had been made. I was to go again last Saturday, but I had no time. I am dreadfully busy with the arrangements for the Annual Prize Day of the School; the Girl Guides are my charge. I am immediately sending the goldsmith's memo to Mr. Talukdar. Please ask him to get the ornaments for you. I have seen the earrings; they look very nice. Can't say about the other ornaments. Haven't got a moment to spare. I beg of you not to write such harsh letters. I feel so unhappy.

Yours,
N A M I T A

Chandrababu sniffed ; the note-paper was mildly scented. He closed his eyes and tried to conjure up the picture of an enraged young beauty, her full lips trembling with emotion. But the picture refused to emerge ; in his mind's eye he could only see the repulsive face of a schoolteacher he knew, a spinster of haggard appearance—dry and pale, with high cheek-bones and a long, thin nose like a curved scimitar.

Damn it all ! Chandrababu opened the second letter. Ah, here's one from a man to his wife.

I have got your letter. If you aren't a little more considerate in these hard days, I'm helpless. Rice is selling at more than forty rupees a maund, pulses are equally dear, so are coal and vegetables. Nilambar told me that flour was twelve annas a seer, and that, too, mixed with soap-stone. Mustard oil is two rupees. As for ghee, I was afraid even to ask the price. One can't have a pair of the most coarse sarees for less than ten rupees, I could not pay cash for everything. Had to buy a number of things from Nilambar on credit. What else could I do? I had to send twenty rupees to Nabin. How can I manage everything? And you must choose this moment to buy longcloth for one rupee a yard. What do you take me for? Nawab Khanja Khan, or what? I am working myself to death to earn a miserable pittance. What does my employer pay me for a month's grinding labour? Not a thousand, nor five hundred, but just seventy-five rupees—not a pie more. Why must you buy *jarda* when it's so expensive. That shop of Profulla's will be my ruin......

What an infernal nuisance ! In sheer annoyance, Chandra-babu knitted his eyebrows and put the letter back into the envelope. Such a boring rigmarole written over full four pages.

The third letter was also in a man's hand. The envelope was of a rosy tint, and addressed to one Nilima Basu. But yet another disappointment. Nilima was not a woman. What an effeminate name for a man !

DEAR NILIMA BABU,

You have left two things here, your cigar-case and the hockey-stick. The report on your urine has just come. I am sending it to you. Yes, sugar has been found, four per cent......

Chandrababu was losing his patience ; he had no time to go through such tripe. He opened the fourth letter. A thick envelope, a man's writing.

A picture dropped out : a most unusual and exciting photo. He had seen many studies in many picture cards, but none quite like this. Chandrababu was thrilled, there was a sparkle of sudden animation in his dull, glassy eyes. He turned to the letter. It was marvellous, he could hardly breathe. At last his labour had been rewarded ; this was the real thing.

A most thorough performance ; Freud, Havelock Ellis, Vat-sayan—none had been left out. What persuasive language, what vivid description ! Chandrababu's nostrils dilated in excitement, his lips trembled. He read the letter, once, twice, thrice—but there was no satiety. He thought of keeping the letter. But that, he pondered, would be wrong. Besides it was not necessary ; he could copy out the salient portions. Even that would be a pleasure—to copy such things. Of course he would not see her for three days, but when he returned home, he would read the extracts to Madhuri. He had done this before. He remembered Madhuri's face. There seemed to be something wrong with her. She was never gay. She sat with a sullen face whenever Chandrababu was near her. Her face was so lovely—that little dimple when she smiled, but she would never smile. Anyway, he would try again, and read out these extracts. He would see if *this* did the trick.

Chandrababu started copying. After writing out the main passages, he went through the original once again. Then he put it back into the envelope. The picture, of course, he would keep.

And now the last letter. A blue envelope with the address of a man typed on it.

Such letters, Chandrababu knew, were often full of un-expected thrills. Some people leave envelopes with their wives with their addresses typed on them. But typists too, have a flair for writing fruity letters. Typewritten addresses, indeed, have possibilities.

Chandrababu took another *pan* with *jarda* and started chewing, his eyes half-closed in a state of dreamy intoxication. The *pan* and *jarda* filled his mouth with saliva. He opened the window to spit it out. Oh, what a night ! The streaks of lightning were frightening ; he closed the window. The fourth letter had put him under a dreamy spell. What expression ! He was sure Madhuri would not be able to resist its effect......

Chandrababu opened the last letter.

DEAREST ANANGA,

I am so glad to know that you'll come. I am waiting for you with an eager heart. This is unbearable, this waiting in this wretched house. Do take me away, I beg of you, wherever you want. I shall be content to live anywhere, in any condition, only if you are with me. But take me away from this hell, that's all I ask of you. Don't be late. The old mug will leave on mail duty by the morning train tomorrow and will be away for three days. I hope you'll be able to reach here tomorrow evening or the next morning. I shall be ready. Countless kisses.

> Yours ever,
> MADHURI

Outside, thunder spoke with a loud crash.

Megh-Mallar

P RADYUMNA met the man at the temple of Dasha-paramita. It was the last day of the month of Jaishtha, and people had come to the temple for the Sankranti Festival. From the neighbouring villages, girls had come to offer *puja*.

All day Pradyumna had looked for the man. Late in the afternoon, when most of the people had gathered round a snake-charmer, he was eagerly watching the assembly, still hoping to find the man he was looking for. He had never met him, but he was sure that there would be something to distinguish the great musician.

Suddenly he noticed a man in the crowd watching him. His clothes were dirty and worn-out, but something in his appearance seemed to tell Pradyumna that this was his man. As Pradyumna made to move toward him, the man beckoned to him to come out of the crowd.

"I am Surdas, the musician from Abanti," said the old man. "Weren't you looking for me ?"

Pradyumna was surprised ; how did he know ?

"You are no stranger to me," the old man said. "Your father was a friend of mine. Whenever I went to Kashi, I made it a point to call on him. I saw you there, but then you were a child."

"Where are you staying here ?" asked Pradyumna.

"In that old and ruined temple near the river. Where do you live ?"

"I am a student at the Vihara here."

"Good. Come and see me. In that temple by the river."

It was not yet dark. The girls were returning home from the temple. Pradyumna was looking at them, his eyes searching for Sunanda. He could not find her and it was getting late. He must return to the Vihara before nightfall—Acharya Sheela-brata was a stern man.

With quick steps, he started walking down the hill. As he came into the open, he could see the dome of the old temple by the river. It stood out against the white clouds tinted with the glow of the setting sun.

Suddenly, he felt some one pull at his clothes. He turned round to see a slim, young girl, dressed in a blue sari. She had a garland of white flowers twined round her dark hair.

"When did you come Sunanda ? I looked for you everywhere, but you weren't to be found."

The girl blushed but sounded hurt as she said, "As if I didn't see what you were doing. You were busy with those magicians and snake-charmers."

"Believe me, Sunanda, I did look for you."

A group of girls was returning from the temple. As they came nearer, Sunanda hurried to join them. Together they went down the slope of the hill. Pradyumna was left behind, disappointed and angry. After a little while, he started again to go back to the Vihara.

The gathering darkness suddenly grew limpid. It was the night of the full moon ; the hills and the surrounding fields were bathed in a soft light, but far afield there was a mellow haze on trees and meadows.

The crowds that had come to the temple slowly melted away. The evening bells were now silent. Pradyumna was hurrying back when he suddenly noticed a human form behind a tree. As he drew near, he found that it was Sunanda, waiting for him. The latticed branches of the tree had drawn a rich pattern of light and shade on her face, her hands, and her blue sari.

"I am really angry with you, Sunanda," Pradyumna said.

"Indeed ? But whose fault was it ? You spent the whole day with the crowd while I was waiting for you in the temple."

"But if you saw me, why didn't you call me ?"

"How could I, with the girls all around ? In the afternoon I was all by myself but you didn't come."

"All right. It was *my* fault. But let me explain. I wasn't after the magicians. I was looking for a great musician from Abanti. You know, Sunanda, how keen I am to learn the *veena*. And this man is really a master. Anyway, I have now met him. Come, let's go and sit by the river. I shall play on the flute. I brought it with me."

They went to the bank of the river, but Pradyumna played absent-mindedly. Sunanda had never seen him so listless before.

He found little inspiration in the music. The strange figure of Surdas haunted him. What an ugly man he was, lean and loose-skinned, almost like the picture of old age drawn by Bhikshu Basubrata ! Even his clothes were dusty red, like old and discoloured parchment.

Next morning, Pradyumna went to the ruined temple by the river. The image of the deity had long disappeared. Gaping cracks in its walls housed numberless snakes.

Surdas said : "Let's go into the open. It's dark inside."

Surdas looked intently at Pradyumna and muttered : "Yes, you will do.   I knew it."

Pradyumna was struck by the stamp of genius in Surdas's ugly face.

Surdas said : "I was hoping you would come. Your father was a famous musician. Did you learn anything from him ?"

"Yes, I can play a little on the flute," Pradyumna said.

"Can you play the *raga* megh-mallar ?"

Pradyumna replied that he had learned the mode, but he could not yet claim any mastery.

"Let's see what you have learned."

Pradyumna took out his flute and began to play. He had a natural gift, and his father had given him careful training. His rendering of megh-mallar was rich and powerful. Perhaps,

Surdas had not expected so moving a recital ; he rose and embraced Pradyumna and said : "Your father would have been proud of you. Yes, you will be able to do it. My instinct was right."

Surdas paused a little, and said : "I have something to tell you, but it's most secret. I may now confess that I, too, was looking for you. It is good we have met. But before I say any more, you must give me your word that you will never give out the secret."

Pradyumna was greatly surprised. He had met the old man only yesterday. What secret could he confide in him? He grew curious and promised not to divulge the secret to anybody.

Surdas lowered his voice and began :

"You can see a mound across the field. In ancient days, there stood on that mound a temple of the goddess Saraswati. This temple had a special virtue. Even now, if a musician, sitting on that mound on the night of the full moon in the month of Asharh, can give a perfect rendering of megh-mallar, the goddess herself appears before him. If he can do so on three successive full-moon nights, he attains complete mastery of his art. By Saraswati's grace, the inmost secret of music is revealed to him. But there is one condition. The musician must be young and unmarried. Why don't you try on the next full-moon night ?"

Pradyumna was listening in utter amazement. He had heard of various Hindu myths about Saraswati, the goddess of learning and the arts. But did she really exist? Was it possible to see her?

"Don't you want to try ?" Surdas asked again.

"Not that. I was only wondering if it's really possible...."

"You can see for yourself. If you have no objection, I will keep everything ready for the next full-moon night."

Pradyumna could hardly think. He seemed to be under a spell. He merely said, "All right. I will come."

On the night of the full moon, Pradyumna accompanied Surdas

to the bank of the river Bhadravati. The sky was overcast but
the darkness seemed liquid in the faint glow of the moon.
Surdas began an elaborate ritual. He filled a skull with oil
and lighted a lamp. Then he lighted the sacrificial fire.
Pradyumna watched the strange, esoteric rites in silent
amazement.

Late at night, when the rites were over, Surdas said : "I
have finished my part of the work, Pradyumna. Now everything rests with you."

Pradyumna was struck by a keen and hungry look in Surdas's
eyes. It made him uneasy, but as he began to play on his flute,
he soon forgot all about Surdas.

There was a hush in the air and the sky. The deep notes of
megh-mallar filled the silence of the night. The spirit of nature
and the spirit of the music were merged in the rhythm of one
single passion.

Suddenly the field was flooded by a soft bright light. In a
halo of white incandescence appeared a young woman of ex-
quisite beauty. Pradyumna could hardly believe his eyes. The
goddess of knowledge and art, the goddess of truth and beauty
was before him. In mute wonder he watched the heavenly
image as it slowly faded back into the air.

Pradyumna stood spellbound. Was this real or was it a
dream ? Was it a fact of experience or a mere figment of over-
wrought fancy ? He had felt the beatific presence, yet he could
not be sure.

He seemed to wake up with a start as Surdas said : "You
believe it now, don't you ? All right, you can go. I have still
some more rites to perform."

Troubled in mind and with a thousand disjointed thoughts,
Pradyumna started back wearily for the Vihara.

It was a long walk. He crossed the fields and entered a wood.
It was very dark. As he was feeling his way through the thick
cluster of trees, he saw a shaft of light through a clearing. It
could not be moonlight. The moon was pale and the sky overcast. As he drew nearer, he could hardly believe what he saw.

The light came from a young woman. Her body was radiant with a peculiar glow, like a firefly on a dark night. And it was the woman he had seen a little while ago. With eyes half-closed, she seemed to be groping her way. Her face had a look of deep distress.

Pradyumna was seized by a strange fear. The whole thing seemed eerie. He quickened his steps and hurried back to the Vihara.

For long he could not sleep. In the early hours of the morning, he had a strange dream. A goddess of incomparable beauty was being drawn into the dark waters of the Bhadravati; she struggled to rise, but the cruel waters drew her back; the glow of her body was fading, and darkness closed on her. A huge fish watched her struggles with a vicious grin; the fish had the ugly face of Surdas.

Next morning, Pradyumna told the whole story to Acharya Purnavardhan of the Mahakotthi Vihara. The old and wise man listened with surprise and growing anxiety. At last, he said: "I feared something like this would happen. Some men are about who would stop at nothing to gain their selfish ends. And you have helped them in their evil deeds; you have been used as a tool in making Saraswati a captive. Now, tell me, what does this man look like?"

Pradyumna described Surdas's lean and hungry features.

"Now I know," said Purnavardhan. "The man is not Surdas, nor is he from Abanti. It's Gunadhya, the *kapalik*."

"Listen Pradyumna," Purnavardhan went on, "about two hundred years ago a young musician lived in that temple of Saraswati. He played megh-mallar with such wonderful skill that the goddess herself often appeared before him. Since then, the goddess has always responded if someone plays megh-mallar perfectly at that site. Once she appeared before Surdas. By her grace, Surdas became the greatest musician in the country. Gunadhya happened to be present. When the goddess offered him a boon, the importunate man demanded the goddess herself. The goddess said he was asking for the impossible and disappeared. Gunadhya, mad with desire, began to learn various Tantric rites in order to gain possession of the goddess. For a long time, we have had no news of him. From what you say, it seems that he has at last carried out his evil design. Go back to that temple by the river and see if he is still there."

Pradyumna rushed back to the temple, but, as he had feared, it was empty. He met Sunanda and told her he was going away on important business but would soon return to her.

That night, he left the Vihara.

A year passed. Pradyumna travelled all over the country in search of the man who had completely upset his life. There was no trace of him. Nobody seemed to have heard of Gunadhya. Strange things were, however, happening in the world of art and learning. Mihirgupta, the famous sculptor, had long been working on an image of the Buddha. The statue, when finished, had none of the serenity of the Master. People were shocked to see a demoniac expression on its face. Yamuna-charya, the renowned scholar of Taxila, had been working for a year on a new interpretation of Mimamsa philosophy. During the twelve months, he had suddenly become confused and had now to start all over again with elementary principles.

Many such reports reached Pradyumna. He had a feeling that he knew what all this meant. He continued his unavailing search for Gunadhya.

One day he heard of a man who had just arrived in the village of Uruvilva. The man, he was told, resembled the *kapalik* he was looking for. He hastened to the village immediately but could not trace the mysterious newcomer.

After searching the whole day, he felt very tired. He had come to the farthest end of the village. He sat under a big banyan tree for a little rest. It was not yet dark, and he looked out at the meadows that stretched before him. The twilight scene was so peaceful, so soothing to his distracted mind. At a little distance stood a hillock; it was covered with wild vegetation, but there was a narrow footpath along its steep incline.

Pradyumna was rather surprised to see a human form emerge from the thick bushes. It was coming down the narrow lane. As it came nearer, he could see it was a young woman coming down the hill to fetch water from a small pond.

Something lighted a vague remembrance. Had he seen the woman before? He went toward the pond to have a closer look.

Was this really possible? Pradyumna wondered. It was the young woman he had seen in the wood near the Mahakotthi Vihara, the goddess who had appeared before him on that fateful night. The same eyes, the same delicate features. But her body had lost all its heavenly glow; she looked unutterably pale.

Pradyumna did not know what to do. He had left the Vihara with a troubled mind and in the excitement of his search he had never foreseen the possibility that had now become real. Perplexed and confused, he slunk away from the place, anxious not to be seen by the woman. But next evening he returned to the spot again to see her fetch water from the pond. He kept up this strange vigil for a few days, still undecided what to do.

One evening, he saw the woman step down into the pond. She was trying to pluck a water-lily but seemed to be afraid of going beyond her depth. As he drew nearer, she saw him and said with a faint smile: "Will you please pluck me that flower?"

"I will, if you give me something to eat. I am very hungry."

"Oh, I am so sorry. Leave that flower. Come to my hut. I'll see what I can offer you."

Pradyumna accompanied the young woman to her cottage on the top of the hillock. She opened the door and said: "Please come in."

Pradyumna saw that there was no one else in the small hut. "Do you live here alone?" he asked.

"No. A sannyasi has brought me here. I don't know what he does. Sometimes he leaves me here alone and returns after five or six days."

The woman filled an earthen bowl with grain soup and gave it to Pradyumna.

"Where were you before? Where is your home?" he asked.

The woman was busy serving rice on a large wooden plate. She looked up, surprised.

"My home? I don't know. I'm told I was lying unconscious in a temple by the road to Vidisha. The sannyasi found me there. I can't remember anything about my past life."

Her mind seemed to be far away. Distrait, she looked out at the evening sky, as if trying to remember something that had completely faded from her memory. Suddenly she began to weep; tears rolled down her pale cheeks.

She wiped her eyes, took the rice plate and gave it to Pradyumna.

"I'm sorry there's nothing else I can give you to eat. But please stay for the night. I shall make some sweets with dried lotus seeds. You can eat them in the morning."

"You are afraid to be all alone here at night, aren't you?"

"Yes. I feel terribly afraid. Something moves in those bushes of wild reeds. I can't sleep."

Pradyumna agreed and stayed the night, most of the time talking with the young woman. He found that she had not the vaguest notion of who she really was.

In the morning he took his leave. But every night he would come and keep watch at the foot of the hillock. Apart from anything else, his brave young heart rebelled at the thought of this helpless young woman being left alone in that lonely hut.

Sometimes he could hear the woman sing, sitting all by herself in the silence of the night. The songs filled him with wonder.

One morning a villager of Uruvilva told Pradyumna that the

man he had been looking for had just been seen bathing in a small pond at the foot of the hillock. He ran to the pond and found the man. Yes, it was the *kapalik*.

Gunadhya was rather taken back; he had not expected to meet Pradyumna again.

"How are you here?" he asked.

"Don't you know *why* I am here?"

"Well," said Gunadhya, "I know what has led you to come after me. I don't want to hide anything from you now. You don't know, Pradyumna, what a torment it has been, this repentance for my evil deed. Every moment of my life now is unbearable agony. But let me tell you what's happened. I learned some secret charms from a sannyasi by which I could hold anybody a captive in my control. But I could not attract anybody by these charms. So I took your help, and when, attracted by your flute, the goddess appeared before you, I held her a captive. I didn't know what I was doing. I was almost mad. And then there was also the curiosity to test the strength of the charms. To tell you frankly, I myself wasn't sure that they would work on a goddess."

"And now?" asked Pradyumna.

"Now I want to undo my evil work. I have just been to the sannyasi again. He has taught me some new *mantras* which can counteract the effects of the charms I have applied. If some water made potent by these *mantras* is thrown on the goddess, she will be freed. But I don't know if it can ever be done."

"Why?" asked Pradyumna, in eager suspense.

"Whoever throws the water will be turned to stone. Don't be angry, Pradyumna. Consider my position. I am damned either way, so I might as well pass the rest of my life without bothering whether the goddess is free or not. After all, I might look forward to another life after death. But if I am turned to stone, nothing is left for me."

Pradyumna remembered the pale face of the young woman in her lonely hut. Without a moment's hesitation, he said: "I will do it."

"Think again," said Gunadhya, quite surprised, "this is no joke."

"Give me that water," Pradyumna said firmly.

He accompanied the *kapalik* to his cottage on the hillock.

"I beg of you," the latter said as they went up the hill, "think again. Don't have any false hopes. Nothing can save you. You will be eternally lost to life. Even the goddess herself won't be able to do anything about it. The *mantras* are irrevocable, even the goddess is not exempt from their inexorable law."

"Please don't worry. Let's go."

On the top of the hill, they found the young woman sitting outside her hut. She seemed pleased to see Pradyumna.

"You know I had been thinking of you since you left. You said you would come again."

As she went inside to get some food for him, Gunadhya asked again: "Are you really serious?"

"Let's not argue. Give me the water."

The woman came out with a plate of sweets for Pradyumna.

After a little while, she took up an earthen pitcher and went down the hillock to fetch water.

"Take this bowl of water," Gunadhya told Pradyumna. "Let me first go away. When the goddess returns, throw this water on her."

He picked up his belongings and went down the hill. Pradyumna sat alone.

He was suddenly stricken by a strong nostalgia. Looking at the evening sky, he remembered his mother waiting for him in their house at Kashi. He remembered Sunanda. Was she, too, thinking of him at this hour? He had never felt so homesick before; he felt a lump in his throat; his eyes were wet.

The young woman was coming up the hill. Pradyumna cast aside all wavering from his mind. As the woman came near, he went up to her, touched her feet, and said:

"I did something very wrong, but I didn't know what I was doing. In any case, I must atone for my sin."

The woman looked at Pradyumna, completely puzzled.

"Can't you really remember where you came from?" asked Pradyumna.

"Why, by that road to Vidisha...."

Pradyumna took the bowl Gunadhya had given him and threw a little water on her.

She seemed to wake up with a start.

Pradyumna threw some more water. For a moment, he was thrilled by a vision of ineffable beauty, a feeling of unutterable joy. Then as his eyes closed, he remembered in a last flash of consciousness the loving face of his mother, looking out of the window in their house at Kashi, eagerly waiting for his return.

A young girl received initiation into the Holy Order of the Lord Buddha from Acharya Sheelabrata of Mahakotthi Vihara. Her name was Sunanda, daughter of Syamantadas, the wealthy merchant of Hiranyanagar. She had refused to marry. Her early renunciation had earned her respect and affection from all inmates of the Vihara. But she always remained sad and distant.

On moonlit nights, she would stand on the stone terrace of the Vihara and keep gazing at the open fields that stretched into the soft haze of the night. Hadn't someone told her that he would come back? Every morning she hoped he would come during the day. And as the day wore on, she waited for his coming in the evening. Evening grew into night; she still waited on the lonely terrace. The slightest rustle of leaves startled her. She looked about, eagerly waiting for footsteps, waiting for the young man whom she loved, the one who said he would come back.

Late at night, when she fell asleep, she sometimes had a strange dream. Somewhere, on the top of a hill, was a stone image. She could not see the face of the image clearly as it was covered by large reeds and bamboo leaves. A strong wind, which blew into the thick cluster of reeds and bamboo branches, produced a kind of music, like the deep strains of megh-mallar.

At the break of day, the dream faded away. As she woke up, the whole thing seemed so unreal, yet so mysterious. In the light of day, she could not explain anything, but she felt she must wait.

MANIK BANDYOPADHYAY

Prehistoric

THE rains had been a trying time for Bhikhu.

In June his whole gang had got rounded up while trying to break into Baikuntha Saha's shop at Basantapur. Of the eleven, Bhikhu alone had been able to make good his escape. With a gaping wound on his left shoulder, he had walked ten miles in the rainy night, hiding himself during the day behind an old bridge with one half of his body below the mud and the other invisible behind the thickets. He had resumed his journey at night and reached his old accomplice Prohlad Bagdi's house eighteen miles away in the village of Chitanpur.

But Prohlad had not given him shelter.

Pointing at the wound he had said, "That wound's not going to heal, brother. It is going to be septic. There will be as great a swelling as you have ever seen. Then suppose people find you out, what shall I do? If you hadn't killed the man—"

"I feel like killing you, Prohlad."

"Sorry, no hope of that, brother."

Faced with Prohlad's refusal, Bhikhu took shelter in the forest lying five miles north of the village. Prohlad took him to the remotest interior of the forest and made him a shed among the thickets with palm-leaves and strips of bamboo. Before going he said, "The tigers have all gone up the hill. They can't stand the rain. If you don't get bitten by snakes, you will be all right."

"But what shall I have to eat?"

"Why, I have given you dried rice and molasses. Every third day I will fetch you some boiled rice. I can't come every day, lest people find out."

Prohlad dressed Bhikku's wound with leaves and creepers and went away, assuring him that he would come again.

In the night, the fever came on, as predicted by Prohlad; and likewise came, next morning, the swelling. The right hand looked like a huge drum. It was impossible to move it even slightly.

So Bhikhu spent two nights and days in that narrow little shed in the depths of a forest in which even tigers refused to live. It was full of mosquitoes and leeches and worms of innumerable kinds, known and unknown. For two days and nights the rain poured down over his head in torrents and unknown creatures fed themselves on his body. Tormented by fever and pain, he turned from side to side, plucking a leech now from his arm, now from his leg, every half hour. When it rained, the water dripped through the meagre roof over his head and wetted him; when the sun shone he sat breathing hard in the sweltering, stifling heat, and the little creatures of the earth who moved around in their vast pleasure garden did not give him a moment's peace. He had finished the tobacco rolls Prohlad had left him. There was still enough dried rice to last three or four days, but no molasses. The molasses had disappeared, but the little red ants who had been attracted by it had not yet left, and it was for Bhikhu to endure the sting of their disappointment all over his body.

He kept on cursing Prohlad from the depth of his bowels and struggled to live. On the morning of the day Prohlad was due to come he found even the earthen jug empty. He waited for Prohlad till the afternoon and then, unable to bear his thirst, took up the jug and dragged himself to the drain running a little away from his shed and came back with a little water, groaning with pain. The exercise, besides increasing his pain, whetted his hunger. He began to munch the plain dried rice somehow to stuff his stomach. Eating with one hand, he kept on killing the ants and worms viciously with the other. But instead of killing the leeches as on the previous day, he picked them carefully from the ground and set them to his

wound, hoping that they would suck in the bad blood and cure
him of his pain. Once, catching sight of a green snake peeping
through the leaves above his head, he sat watching, stick in
hand, for two hours, and then started beating at the bushes
all around, making loud noises all the while with his tongue.

No, he must not die. He just must not let himself die, even if,
man as he was, he had to be in a state in which even beasts
could not live.

Prohlad had been to another village for the marriage of a
relation. After the day's festivities, he had helped himself to
his fill of strong country liquor, which kept him blissfully
unaware, for three days, of what was happening to Bhikhu.

Bhikhu's wound turned septic, and the brownish yellow
pus was running down his chest and back. The rest of his body
had also swollen up a little. The fever had come down but a
tearing pain filled his whole body. Like strong liquor it slowly
made him limp and threw him into a drowsy stupor. He no
longer felt hunger or thirst. The leeches crawled up his body
and drank of his blood and fell off of themselves without his
knowing when they had swollen into red balls looking like
small, fresh tomatoes. A chance kick from his foot rolled the
earthen jug down to the ground and broke it. The dried rice,
wetted by the rain, began to rot, and in the night hungry foxes
began to circle about his shed, attracted by the rancid smell
emitted by his sores.

Back from the marriage feast Prohlad shook his head gravely
on seeing Bhikhu's condition. He had brought a bowl of boiled
rice, a few bits of fried fish, and a little curry, but since Bhikhu
did not appear to be in any condition to eat, he ate the food
up himself. Toward evening he went home and brought back
a ladder and his brother-in-law, Bharat.

They laid Bhikhu on the ladder and carried him home and
made him a bed of straw on the high platform in Prohlad's
room.

And such was the vigour of life in Bhikhu that even this
meagre improvement in conditions gave him the needed

chance. Fighting against almost inevitable death, he gradually got the better of it, without medicine, nursing, or proper diet, and within one month. But his right hand he could not cure. Like the dead branch of a tree it shrivelled and dried up and became inert. At first he could move it a little, but even this meagre strength it gradually lost.

After the sore had healed, Bhikhu often fetched himself down the ladder with the left hand when no one was about, and one evening he did something which caused a great row.

Prohlad was not at home at the time. He was out, in the company of Bharat, for a spot of liquor. His sister was at the riverside, bathing. Prohlad's wife had come in to lay her little son on the bed. She caught sight of Bhikhu's hungry eyes and was trying to get away when Bhikhu leaped forward and avidly seized her by the arm.

But Prohlad's wife was a Bagdi, the famous caste that has given Bengal the majority of her highwaymen and her fighters. It was not as easy to lay hands on her as Bhikhu had imagined. He had reckoned without the feeble state of his health and the absence of his right arm. With one shake she freed herself and went away, abusing him heartily. When Prohlad came home, she told him everything.

His groggy, beery head told Prohlad that there was nothing to it but to kill the ungrateful wretch. So after giving his wife a cracking blow on her back, he turned upon Bhikhu. But it was clear to him even in his boozy state that the task of killing Bhikhu outright was not so easy to carry out. For Bhikhu stood ready to receive him, a sharp hatchet in his hand and a fixed look in his eyes. So instead of flying at each other's throats as duty would have it, they emptied their stock of bad language on each other and left it there, unwillingly enough.

At the end of it Prohlad said, "I spent seven rupees on you. Give that back to me and clear out of my house."

"I had a gold chain round my waist. You stole it. Give that back and I will go."

"I know nothing about any gold chain of yours."

"I tell you Prohlad, give me back that chain if you want to avoid trouble. If you don't I will hack off your head from your shoulders, just as I did to that Saha fellow of the bazar. If you give it to me, I will get out of here without a word."

But Bhikhu never got back his gold chain. Bharat appeared on the scene, and between him and Prohlad they managed Bhikhu properly enough. Beyond tearing some flesh of Prohlad's arm with his teeth, Bhikhu could hardly do anything. They beat him up soundly and left him half dead. Bhikhu's healing wound burst open and the blood began to trickle down his back again. Wiping it awkwardly with the back of his hand, he limped away into the darkness. No one knew where he went. But in the middle of the night there was a row, and the whole neighbourhood woke up to find Prohlad's house going up in flames.

Prohlad struck his forehead with his palm and complained bitterly against Fate that had been so unkind to him. But for fear of the police, he could not open his mouth to name Bhikhu even once.

The second chapter of Bhikhu's life had begun.

After setting fire to Prohlad's house, he had stolen a fisherman's boat that carried him downstream on the river that flowed by Chitanpur. He was too weak to row. The whole night he sat at the helm just keeping the boat straight with the help of a flat piece of bamboo. He had not got very far when the sun rose.

He feared that Prohlad would give him away, forgetting his own danger in his itch for revenge. For a long time now, the police had been after him, and since the murder at the bazar, their efforts had doubled. After Prohlad had told on him, they would be on the lookout for him everywhere. It was impossible for him to make an appearance anywhere within forty miles of the place. But he had grown desperate. For two days now he had not eaten anything: his weak body was still shrunken with pain from the blows the two hefty men had showered on him. Early in the morning he pulled up before the river ghat of the district town. Dipping himself several times in the river, he washed away the stains of blood and then got up and walked in. Hunger was gnawing within him and making him feel dizzy. He had not even a pice with which to buy himself some fried rice. So he held out his palm to the first gentleman he saw and said, "Give me two pice, sir."

The man turned and ran his eyes down Bhikhu. He gave him a pice, pitying him perhaps for his ragged hair, his loin cloth, and his shrunken arm.

"Just one, sir?" Bhikhu protested. "Give me two."

"What!" the man exclaimed angrily, "Not pleased with one, eh? Get away!"

For a second Bhikhu felt like filling the babu's nice ears with all the hot, foul words at his command, but on second thoughts he restrained himself. Casting a burning look at the man, he turned and went to the shop before him and bought a piceworth of fried rice and began to gulp it down.

This was the first time he had begged.

But his apprenticeship at this ancient trade did not have to last long. In a few days' time he was perfect master of its code of etiquette and its many techniques of appeal. To see him one would think he was a beggar by birth. He no longer washed himself. He let his hair gather into masses of rough, greasy knots, till it came to be colonised by a prosperous family of lice. At times they made him mad and with his claws he scratched his head wildly and nearly tore out his hair, but he dared not crop it. His scar he hid below a coat, which he had earned by begging and which, even in the sultriest weather, he did not remove. The right sleeve of his coat had to be cut off, however, for it hid his best asset, the shrivelled arm. When, after all this, he was able to get together a tin mug and a stick, he knew he had reached perfection itself.

From morning till evening he sat under a tamarind tree near the bazar and begged. His breakfast consisted of one-piceworth of fried rice, but at midday he would get into an old abandoned orchard near the place and, seated below a banyan tree, cook himself some rice and curry, sometimes also a little fish. After he had eaten his fill, he would sit leaning against the banyan tree and puff away at a little roll of tobacco leaf for a while.

The whole day he sat appealing to the mercy of passers-by, "Give me a pice, O my lords! God will give you double what you give me. Give me a pice or two!" To add to his powers of attracting pity, he punctuated his sentences with quick, heavy breaths, like those of an asthmatic.

During the whole day more than a thousand men passed Bhikhu, and, on an average, every fiftieth man, tossed him a pice or half-pice coin. His usual income stood at about eight annas a day, although when there were too many half-pice coins, it did occasionally come down to five or six annas. On the two market days in the week, it never fell below one rupee.

The rains had now passed. The banks of the rivers were white with blossoms of *kasha* waving in the wind. Near this idyllic spot stood Bhikhu's shed adjoining the house of Binnu the fisherman who had rented it out to him. Its roof was leaky and its creaking doors were ready to fall to pieces but, as long as it did not rain, it gave good shelter and Bhikhu slept blissfully in it. There was no lack of comfort for him, for he had an ancient quilt sewn out of rags that he had taken from the body of a man who had died of malaria. He had also stolen hay from haystacks here and there and gradually come to have a fairly thick heap on which he slept luxuriously. He had gone out to beg at the neighbouring houses and, at one house, had been given some torn clothes. These he rolled up into a pillow and laid his head on it. If there was a cool breeze, he took out a piece from the bundle and snugly wrapped himself in it.

Living in such happy circumstances, with plenty to eat every day, Bhikhu recovered his former strength before long. His chest expanded, the muscles on his limbs danced with every movement. His new strength filled him and began to

overwhelm him. The constant need to repress his energy began
to shorten his temper and whet his impatience. He still begged
in his well-learned ways, but he seethed with rage when someone refused him or took no notice of him. When the streets
were empty he hurled bad language at the indifferent. At
times buying something at a shop, he would demand a little
extra and brandish his enormous fist at the shopkeeper if he
was not given it instantly. When the women came to the river
to bathe he stood watching them, pretending to beg; when
they asked him to go, he only grinned rakishly. He laughed
with malicious delight when they showed fear.

In the nights he tossed restlessly on his self-made bed.

Soon he began to hate his cheerless existence. Hotly desiring
the flesh of woman, he longed to go back to life as it had once
been—wild, eventful, and reckless.

His mind travelled back to the past. Memories stood up
before him of drunken evenings followed by midnight raids
on rich households in the company of his old trusted comrades,
of scenes of wild hacking and killing concluded by triumphant
escapes. Was there anything more fascinating in the world
than to see, under the glaring light of a burning torch, the
wild look on a wife's face when you whacked away at her
husband or to hear her scream when the blood spurted out
of her son's young body? When he had run from village to
village escaping from the police and lived in dense forests and
hills it had been bad enough, but not worse than this. Many
of his gang had been caught several times and served long
terms behind the bars but, except for once, the police had not
been able to lay hands on him. They had caught him the time
he and Raghu Bagdi had run away with that pretty sister of
Sripati Biswas, but he had served only two out of the seven
years given him. Jumping over the high wall of the jail one
rainy evening, he had made away and baffled the police in all
their attempts to put him back into jail. Thereafter he had
broken into a house, seized a married woman near a pond in
broad daylight, relieved her of her necklace and bangles, and,

with Raghu Bagdi's wife, fled to Hathia across the sea, past Noakhali. Six months later he had thrown off the woman, and back on the mainland, he formed three gangs, one after another, and made innumerable raids on all sorts of villages of which he could not even remember the names now. And only the other day he had hacked the head of Baikuntha Saha's brother into two neat slices with one blow.

To think of what his life had been, and what it was now!

His chief pleasure had once been killing; now he had to be content with merely abusing a man who refused to toss him a coin. His strength he had got back in full, only pity was that he had not the means to apply it. He had seen shopkeepers counting their cash late in the night. He was sure there were plenty of houses in which women slept alone and defenceless.

Lying there in the dark Bhikhu stroked the stump of his right arm and his vexation knew no bounds. Here he was lying as good as dead in a fisherman's hut just for the lack of an arm, when all around him swarmed thousands of weak-kneed, timid men and women just waiting to be seized! Was it possible that one should have such ill luck?

At the entrance to the bazar a beggar woman had her chosen seat. She was young and her body was well formed and agile. But from the knee to the ankle of her right foot extended a festering sore, which she never tried to heal as it gave her an advantage over most of the other beggars, including Bhikhu. At times Bhikhu went up to her, squatted by her side, and asked: "That sore isn't going to heal, is it?"

"Why not?" answered the woman. "It would soon heal if I put some medicine on it."

"Then heal it; get the medicine and heal it. It will do you good. You won't have to go about begging; I will keep you."

"Who told you I was going to live with you for the asking?"

"Why shouldn't you? I will get you your food and cloth, you will live like a queen, just sit with legs crossed and do nothing. You say no to a man who wants to marry you?"

But the woman was not so easy to lay. Thrusting some tobacco leaves into her mouth she said, "Hm! And when you get rid of me after two days, who will give me back my sore?"

Bhikhu promised life-long devotion and held up the prospects of a bright future. But she did not agree, in spite of the ardour of his wooing. Bhikhu walked back to his seat, disappointed.

This happened many times.

To add fuel to the flames consuming him, the moon rose every night in a clear sky, in the river the tides came and the early winter sun spread a faint, luxurious warmth over everything. In the banana orchard next to Bhikhu's shed, the last bananas sold out. Binnu the fisherman bought his wife a new waistband. The magic of country liquor grew richer and deeper. Bhikhu's love overcame his loathing.

Early one morning he went straight to the beggar woman. "Come," he said, "the sore won't matter after all. Let's—"

"Why, what were you doing so long?" The woman jeered at him, "Go and hang yourself; stuff your mouth with ash!"

"What's that talk about eating ash?"

"You think I have been sitting waiting for you so long, do you? There, I'm with that man, over there."

She pointed at a stout, bearded but lame beggar sitting a little away from the place. Like his own right arm the man's right foot had shrivelled, up to his knee. Displaying it with special care, he sat appealing to everybody in the name of Allah.

By his side lay a short, wooden, artificial leg.

"So still sitting by me you are, eh? Run along quick. If he sees you, he'll kill you off straight," continued the beggar woman.

"Oh, keep that joke to yourself! Any blasted rogue can come and kill me off when he likes, eh? I'm good enough for ten like him, see?"

"Then go and pick a quarrel with him, if you dare. Why waste your time on me?"

"Leave him, I say. Come with me."

"O my darling prince! Have some tobacco, dear? You turned up your nose at my sore, remember? Now you think I'll let you hang around me and make friends with me, you fool! Why should I leave him and go to you? Do you earn half as much as he? Have you got a room to yourself? Get out of here or I'll let you have a taste of my tongue, I will."

Bhikhu laid off for the moment, but did not give up hope. As soon as he found her alone again, he went up and began, "What is your name, eh?"

They had never thought of asking one another's names before this.

Baring her black teeth, the beggar woman smiled. "After me again? There, go to that old woman!"

Bhikhu squatted down by her side, undaunted. From out of the bag slung from his shoulder he took a huge banana and said, "Come, take that. I stole it from an orchard for your sake." He carried a bag these days as many people gave handfuls of rice instead of money.

The woman peeled the banana and swallowed her lover's gift without wasting any time. She seemed pleased with its taste. She said, "You want to know my name? They call me Panchi. Panchi—see? You gave me a banana, so I told you my name. Now run along."

But Bhikhu would not budge. He was not generous enough to take so little for so much. Squatting there on the ground he went on trying to make himself at home with Panchi in words and phrases that to many would seem abuse.

Panchi's man was called Basir. One day Bhikhu tried to make his acquaintance. "Good day, mister," he began.

"Why do you hang about here, eh? Goodday, mistering me! Crack your head with this stick, I will."

There was a noisy row, which lasted for a few minutes but did not end up in fighting as both the men were properly armed, Bhikhu with a huge stone and Basir with his stick.

Turning to go back to his seat below the tamarind tree, Bhikhu said, "You wait. I will finish you off before long."

"If you hang about her again, I will just chop you into bits, by Allah I swear."

Bhikhu's earnings had begun to drop.

New men did not walk along the road everyday. The number of those who did soon dwindled to a few among those who lived in those parts. Many of them had already shown their pity once or twice and did not feel any urge to give more. There was no lack of beggars in the world, after all.

Bhikhu earned just enough to keep himself alive. Except on market days he could not save a single pie out of his earnings. He was worried.

It would be difficult to live in that shed in the winter. He must get a room somehow. He did not care what it was like as long as it had four walls. No young beggar woman would agree to live with him unless he could give her two square meals a day and a roof to live under. Yet his income was dwindling at such a rate that with the coming of winter he would hardly be able to buy a meal for himself.

He must raise his income, no matter how.

But he could not imagine how he would set about this, for he could not steal or rob, or even work, with one hand. He could not even hold up a man and take his purse. On the other hand he could not think of leaving the town without Panchi. His mind revolted against the cruelty of fate, and he burned with envy to see the happy family life of his neighbour, the fisherman. At times he itched to set fire to the house and ruin the nice little household. He walked about on the riverside aimlessly and decided that until he had killed all the men and seized all the women of the world there would be no peace for him.

He passed a few more months with this discontent smouldering within him.

Late one night he packed his more valuable things into his bag, rolled up the few rupees he had saved in a long piece of cloth, tied it tightly round his waist, and stepped out. He had picked up an iron rod at the riverside one evening and sharpened one end of it in his spare time till it had become a serviceable spear-like weapon. This also he put in his bag.

Stars gleamed in the dark sky. It was the night before the new moon. On God's earth there was profound quiet. Coming out into his familiar world of the dark, silent, and deserted night with the thrill of a terrible purpose within him, Bhikhu's mind burst with a new-found exultation, an overwhelming sense of release. "I wish you had spared my right arm and taken the left, God!" he suddenly cried into the night raising his eyes towards the starlit sky.

He walked along the riverside for about half a mile and then entered the town through a narrow lane. Walking past the bazar on his left, he plunged into a maze of lanes and by-lanes and tortuous alleys and reached the outskirts of the sleeping town. The macadamised road to the district town began at this point. The river, meandering a long distance, ran parallel to the road for a mile from here and then changed its course again.

The road was dotted with houses here and there for a distance after which came the paddy fields interspersed with patches of fallow land overgrown with bushes. In a clearing in one of these stood a few sheds put up by an assortment of tramps, one of whom was Basir. He rose early in the morning and clattered all the way to town to beg. When he was back at his hovel in the evening, he sat puffing at a hubble-bubble while Panchi started a fire with dried leaves and boiled some rice. After they had eaten and Panchi had wrapped a rag round her sore, the two stretched side by side on a bamboo cot and whispered in their strange inhuman dialect till they fell asleep. From their nest and their beds and bodies arose a putrid smell which stole through the chinks in the thatched roof and mingled with the outer air.

Basir snored in his sleep. Panchi muttered incoherently. Bhikhu had taken care to follow them one day and spot their hovel. He stood on tiptoe in the knee-high jungle of arum, his ears glued to the cane wall, listening. Then he tiptoed round to the front. The door, woven out of straw and rushes, was not fastened from inside. Panchi had just closed it lightly before going to bed. It was only a beggar's hut.

Bhikhu moved the door carefully to one side, took out the sharpened rod, and, holding it firmly in his hand, went in. Outside the hut there had been the starlight. Here it was all dark. He had not the required number of hands to strike a match. Standing there in the dark, he pondered over the problem and realised that it would not be possible to spot the exact location of Basir's heart. Hitting with the left hand he might miss and give Basir an opportunity to kick up a row. That would mean trouble.

He thought for a few moments more, and then with one sudden powerful stroke thrust the sharpened end of the rod about three inches into the sleeping man's head. In the dark there was no way of knowing the extent of the injury. Trying to feel with his hand he found that the rod had gone in a good length. To make doubly sure, with his one hand he seized Basir's throat with all his might and strangled him.

To Panchi he said, "Keep quiet. If you cry I will kill you, too, like him there."

Panchi merely groaned with fear.

"Not a sound," Bhikhu warned her again, "if you don't want to be killed too !"

At last Basir's body became quite still. Bhikhu removed his hand from his throat.

Releasing his breath with a grunt, he said, "Panchi, light the lamp." Panchi obeyed him dumbly. Bhikhu stood looking at the dead body, contemplating his performance with great satisfaction. His pride knew no bounds. With one stroke of his left hand he had killed that big fellow.

Turning to Panchi, he said, "Do you see that? See who killed whom? How many times I told him, 'My dear fellow, you can't go on eating off my plate, give it up.' But what does he do? He's annoyed, 'I'll smash your head', he says. Now come, my darling prince, smash my head, pray smash it, here it is!"

Bhikhu bowed his head ironically before the dead man. Then throwing it back, he laughed. Suddenly he flew into a rage and said, "Why don't you say something, eh ? Are you dumb? Speak! Do you want me to finish you off too?"

Trembling all over Panchi asked feebly, "What will you do now?"

"Wait and see," Bhikhu chuckled. "First tell me where he hid his money."

Panchi had discovered the spot with great difficulty and at first she pleaded ignorance. But when Bhikhu came up and seized her hair she hurried to show him the place.

Basir's lifelong savings were not meagre. In rupee and half rupee coins they amounted to more than one hundred rupees. There was a time when Bhikhu used to earn much more by killing one man. Yet he was pleased. "Pack up all you want to take along, Panchi. We will get out before night is over. The moon will be up soon and we can get across in the light."

Panchi did as she was told. Then she limped out of the hut, her hand held in Bhikhu's, and set foot on the road. Bhikhu looked up at the eastern sky and said, "The moon will be up soon, Panchi."

"Where shall we go?" asked Panchi.

"To the district town. I will steal any boat we see on the river. In the morning we will hide ourselves in the jungle near Sripatipur and get to town in the night. Now hurry, Panchi, we have two miles to walk."

With the huge sore hurting her, Panchi found it impossible to walk faster. Bhikhu noticed it and stopped.

"Is your leg hurting you, Panchi?" he asked.

"Yes."

"Shall I take you on my back?"

"How can you?"

"Oh, I can."

Panchi put her arms round Bhikhu's neck and clung to his back. Bending forward under her weight, Bhikhu stepped on briskly.

A half moon arose from behind the trees and touched the paddy fields with a faint grey light. On God's earth there was profound quiet.

SARADINDU BANERJEE

The Divine Image

I

THE picture that the term "Buddhist monk" conjures
in our mind hardly fits the features of an average
Bengali of today. Yet Bhikshu Aviram about whom I wish to
write was a Bengali by birth and appearance.

At the start I may say that I have no wish to record the
entire life story of Bhikshu Aviram. I could not do so even if
I wanted to. I never knew his ancestry or caste, nor was I
aware how he, a Bengali, had found his way into a Buddhist
monastery. All I want to set before the reader, briefly and
without exaggeration, is the impression I gathered of his character during our brief acquaintance. And how, one day, in circumstances one could hardly believe, our acquaintance came
to an end. Our country is well known for religious fanaticism.
I have seen many heads broken in the name of religion, but
never before had I seen such religious devotion. Nor is there
much chance that I shall see it again.

I first met him in the Imperial Library. It was about four
years ago. I had just started dabbling in the history of the
Buddhist era. Searching for a rare Buddhist book I found he
had collared it before me. Gradually our acquaintance grew.

He was lean and shaven-headed, his dress lightly tinged
with saffron; in age he was probably under forty. He was very
pleasant in conversation and a smile always clung to his thin
face. There was about him a stamp of undisturbed detachment
often found in a truly religious man. One could not ignore
him as commonplace. Looking into his eyes, one could sense

the glow of a powerful and irrepressible desire. He had neither
hair shirt nor matted locks. Yet, seeing him, one was reminded
of the mad man in Tagore's "Touchstone":

With lips tight-pressed and barred inner door;
He keeps a fierce glow burning in his eyes;
His eyes, like fireflies of the night forever flying
Search for something by their own light.

I had not thought that there could be a Bengali Buddhist
Bhikshu in the present age. I was attracted to him at first
sight and our acquaintance gradually ripened into friendship.
He began dropping in at our house at odd hours. In Buddhist
history his knowledge was not so deep as in Buddhist theology.
Whenever he learned something new about the Buddha he
would come to tell me. There was no end to his curiosity about
my own historical research. He would sit for hours listening
to my discourse, and a ceaseless fire glowed in his eyes.

He had no inhibitions about food. He accepted both fish
and meat without demur. On my asking one day, he said with
a faint smile, "I am a monk and must take whatever is dropped
into my begging bowl. I have no right to pick and choose. Once
a disciple of the Buddha put pork in his bowl—he ate even
that." The man's eyes had suddenly filled with tears.

After six or seven months I came to learn the innermost
desire of his heart. We were discussing Buddhist art at our
house. Bhikshu Aviram said that though there were millions
of Buddha figures in India and outside, all were in the contemplative attitude. Devout artists had carved in stone the
form in which they imagined the Buddha. His true features
they never knew.

"I think they did," I said. "You must have noticed that all
Buddha figures are similar in outline. Of course there are slight
variations but on the whole one can discover a likeness—
elongated ears, curly hair, robust build—in all figures. What
could be the reason? Surely the artists knew his real appearance.

So much similarity could not be based on imagination. They must have had a real model."

Bhikshu Aviram heard me with close attention and was silent for a while. Then slowly he said, "I wonder. There were no images of the Buddha made in his lifetime. Sculpture was not common. Buddha figures begin from the Gupta era, in the fourth century A. D., that is almost 900 years after the Buddha's death. How did men keep alive the memory of his appearance through those 900 years? The Buddhist scriptures give no description of his features. The likeness you mention is perhaps an artistic convention. Some talented artist first fashioned the contemplative figure which was imitated through the ages."

The monk heaved a sigh, "No, man has forgotten his true appearance. There are stone images of Tuten Khamen and Amen Khotep but of the Buddha's divine face there is no likeness."

"Yes," I agreed, "those who have no claims to our memory have left their shapes carved in stone while the supermen are immortal only in men's hearts. Take Christ, for instance. No one knows what he looked like in real life."

"That is true. Yet thousands go on pilgrimage every year to see a vestment he once wore. If they could find his true image, what do you think they would do—they would probably go mad with joy."

Just then I happened to look at his eyes. The expression they held was that of a fanatic. They burned with the fierce absorption that transforms men into martyrs. His eyes were indeed turned toward me, but his mind, it seemed, was trying to pierce the thick fog of 2500 years, searching the radiant image of a divine man.

Suddenly he spoke again, "I have seen the tooth, the hair, and the nails of the Buddha. For some days, I was overwhelmed with joy. But I could not remain satisfied. How did he look? What was the expression in his eyes? Kings left their thrones and came out into the streets to follow him. Housewives left husbands and children to become nuns at his bidding; if only

I could hear the sweet cadence of that voice...."

The Bhikshu could speak no more. His whole body trembled, and, unknown to him, tears streamed down his lean cheeks. I was stunned. I had not thought that one could be so moved with so little reason. I had of course heard that for some Vaishnavas the very name "Krishna" was enough to send them into a trance, but then I never believed it. Witnessing the monk's wonderful ecstasy, I no longer thought such things impossible. I had never come across this aspect of religion. It was as if the scales fell suddenly from my eyes.

Oblivious of everything, the Bhikshu went on, "Gautama, thou emancipated one, I do not want deliverance, I do not want Nirvana—show me once your natural self, show me the divine form in which you walked this earth, O Buddha...."

II

R E L I G I O U S fervour is contagious. Unconsciously, it affected me. That is why, a few days after the incident, while thumbing through the account of Fa Hien, my glance stopped at a particular place. I jumped up in joy and excitement. I had read Fa Hien many times before but how was it I missed this? That afternoon Bhikshu Aviram came. Curbing my excitement I handed him the book. He eagerly asked, "What is this?" "Read," I said and indicated the page. The monk began reading while I watched his face.

Twelve hundred paces south of Vaishali, Sudatta, King of the Vaisyas, had built a south-facing vihara. It was a beauteous spot with clear, full lakes and many trees and flowers. This was the Jetavan Vihara. When the Buddha, arriving at the thirty-third heaven, preached for ninety days for the welfare of his mother, Prasenjit, anxious to see him, prepared a sandalwood image and placed it where the Buddha used usually to sit. When the Lord Buddha returned from heaven the image went to meet him. The Lord then said to the image, "Return to your own place. After my Nirvana you will be the ideal for my four ranks of disciples." At this the image returned. This was the very first image of Lord Buddha, and later images have been modelled on it.

After the Lord's Nirvana the Jetavan Vihara was once reduced to ashes by a fire. The kings and their subjects feared the sandalwood image had been destroyed, but, four or five days later, when a small door of the eastern vihara was opened, the image was seen. A second storey was constructed and the image restored to its old place.....

As one bemused, the Bhikshu dragged his eyes from the book and asked in halting voice, "Where is that image?" "I don't know," I said, "I can't remember seeing any mention of the sandalwood image anywhere else." Thereupon we sat quietly for a long time.

I could imagine how this piece of information had shaken the Bhikshu's innermost being. I had half expected an outburst of joy. I was also curious to see how he would react to this unexpected discovery. He did nothing. He sat still for about half an hour and suddenly stood up. There was a hypnotised expression in his eyes. He looked nowhere. Just as a sleepwalker leaves his bed and goes mechanically out, he left the room.

For about three months I did not see him.

About the end of December, he returned and shook the foundations of my being in a manner beyond my imagination. I still find it difficult to believe that I could ever have resolved to go on so intrepid an adventure.

"I have found it!" he cried.

"Come in and sit down," I said welcoming him joyously.

He would not sit. In a voice full of excitement, he went on, "I have found it, Bibhuti Babu. That image is not lost; it is still there.

"Good Heavens, where did you find it?"

"I have not actually recovered it yet. I have been to Besar where the ruins of ancient Vaisali lie scattered. Nothing remains of the Jetavan Vihara but heaps of brick and stone. Yet there I have found the clue. The image exists."

"How could you trace it?"

"From a stone inscription; a stone had slipped out from a ruined temple, and this was the inscription on its reverse."

He handed me a piece of paper and continued, "After the

destruction of Jetavan Vihara, a temple was built out of its stones. The temple itself is 600 years old with no deity there now. A huge peepal tree has coiled round it like a python and is crushing its ribs and bones to dust. The stones are tumbling down. On one such stone was carved this inscription."

I took the paper from his hand and examined it. It was an inscription in the Prakrit of the tenth or eleventh century which the Bhikshu had copied exactly.

Deciphering was not very difficult. The stone's message was as follows :

Alas, O Lord, evil days have now befallen the true religion. How terrible is the state of Jetavan Vihara where you spent twenty-five years. Householders no longer give alms to your monks. The Kings are disrespectful to the vihara. No more do students come from the ends of the earth to study Buddhist philosophy. The glory of the Lord's religion is departed.

Over and above this a terrible danger threatens. For some time past there are rumours that a fierce people called the Turusks have attacked the State. They are heathens who murder priests at sight and loot viharas and monasteries.

The Great Abbot of Jetavan Vihara is sorely troubled at these reports. The Turusks are advancing in this direction. They will surely attack the vihara. The inhabitants are devotees of *ahimsa*, unschooled in arms. Many priceless jewels are stored in the vihara. The most priceless of all is the sandalwood image of the Buddha, which Prasenjit made during the lifetime of the Lord. Who is to protect all these from the Turusk incursion?

After three days and nights of continuous thought, the Abbot has found a way. At midnight, on the coming New Moon, ten monks will depart with the jewels, priceless manuscripts, and the sandalwood image of the Lord. Twenty miles north of the vihara, near a waterfall in the foothills of the Himalayas, there is a stone column constructed by architects from the country of the Asuras. At the top of this column is a secret chamber. It is said that the Asuras built it in the time of the Emperor Asoka (Beloved of the Gods) in the unstable foothills of the Himalayas. The monks will protect the sandalwood image and other articles of value by hiding them in the pillar and will bring them back when the Turusk disturbances are over.

In case the vihara is destroyed in the attack and all here meet death, this inscription is carved on the thirteenth day after the Full Moon by order of the Great Abbot for the knowledge of posterity. May the will of Lord Buddha be fulfilled.

Here the inscription ended. As I read my mind too was in a whirl. I went back eight hundred years and could see in my mind's eye the troubled restlessness of the gentle monks of Jetavan Vihara. The grave, sad face of the Abbot also rose before my vision. The inscription brought to me vividly that historic crisis in India's fortunes. I saw as in a moving picture the countrywide terror. The sudden raid upon a peace-loving, non-martial race by turbulent, merciless foreigners. In my ears rang the concerted cry of a thousand terrified voices, "The Turusk, the Turusk! There come the Turusks!"

Then the vision was shattered. Bhikshu Aviram's eyes were full of triumph.

With a sigh I said, "The Venerable Abbot's wish is fulfilled—but after how long."

In vibrant tones he countered, "Never mind the delay. The time is not yet over. Bibhuti Babu, one thousand five hundred years ago Chinese pilgrims set out on foot from Korea. They travelled across the Gobi desert, covered the mighty Himalayas to come to India. Why? Simply to visit the birthplace of Lord Buddha. And we know the Lord's actual likeness lies within twenty miles of us. Can we not find it?"

"Certainly, you will," I said.

His glowing eyes pierced me as the Bhikshu asked a tremendous question. "Bibhuti Babu, won't you come with me?"

For a moment I was robbed of words. Shall I go? Casting aside work and responsibilities, shall I wander in forest and mountain in search of this illusion?

With throbbing voice the monk continued, "For eight hundred years no one has seen that divine image. Inside that column, the Lord Buddha has waited for eight centuries—for us. Won't you come?"

I don't know what there was in the monk's words, but all my distaste for travel, all my weakness for home and its comforts snapped like the string of a violin when we strike too high a note.

I rose, clasped the Bhikshu's hand and said, "I shall come."

III

WE REACHED a tiny hamlet one afternoon two weeks after leaving Calcutta. It was so high and remote from human habitation that it might have been mistaken for an eyrie in the bosom of the Himalayas. We had not reached the snowline, but the snowy peaks were right in front of us. On all sides were naked hills. Beneath our feet were rocks and gravel. A mountain stream rushed downward at headlong speed through a cleft in the rocks.

As the three of us—Bhikshu Aviram, a Bhutiya guide, and myself—approached the village, all the inhabitants, men, women, and children came out. No one from the outside world ever came there. They gazed at us in wide-eyed wonder. From their features they seemed Lepchas or Bhutiyas. There was also some mixture of Aryan blood. We noticed aquiline noses here and there.

An elderly man with sharp features came forward and said something in his own language, which we could not understand. Our Bhutiya companion explained that this man, the village headman, wished to know why we had come.

We told him frankly why we had come. At first surprise and then intense curiosity were evident on his face. He invited us into the village and we followed, the headman first, then the three of us and the whole village population, young and old, bringing up the wake.

The headman ushered us into a cottage. As we were tired and hungry, he brought us food and drink. Rested and satisfied, we began to talk through our Bhutiya interpreter. The sun had by then hidden behind the mountains, but the long Himalayan evening was full of a crimson glow.

Eight miles north of the village, the headman said, was the

waterfall from which the Upala River began. It was a most remote spot and difficult to climb to. By the waterfall, on the other bank of the river, was a peak which looked like a column and was famed as the Buddha column. On full moon nights villagers worshipped the column, but as it was difficult to reach, no one ever went to it. Instead, they floated their offerings in the river near the village.

The Bhikshu asked if there was any way across the stream to the column. The headman replied that there was a way, but it was so dangerous that no one dared to use it. An ancient iron chain linked the two banks near the waterfall, but it was old and rusty and no one dared to cross over it. Yet it was the only way.

There was no question that we had reached our destination. Yet, to remove all doubt, I asked the headman, "Can no one say what is in that column?"

He said: "No one has ever seen what is there, but the legend from times immemorial runs that the Lord Buddha himself inhabits it. The perfume of sandal forever emanates from his body. After five thousand years, he will again emerge in human form."

The Bhikshu glanced at me. His eyes shone and he exclaimed: "The Lord Buddha himself dwells in the column; the perfume of sandal is forever wafted from his body—do you understand the meaning of the legend? The monks who brought the image probably could not return, perhaps they stayed behind in this very village."

He could not finish. The cottage suddenly started to shake and creak and groan. We were sitting on the floor, and the earth beneath us trembled violently. I scrambled to my feet and shouted, "Earthquake."

By the time we got out, the tremors had ceased. The headman sat calmly on the floor. He smiled at our panic and assured us there was no cause for fear. Such tremors occurred four or five times a day. In fact, the country is called the "birthplace of earthquakes."

We started in surprise. The "birthplace of earthquakes." What a strange name and who knows what terrible, wild child would come to birth out of the earth's violent labours.

But the Bhikshu excitedly said, "Yes—yes, it's mentioned in the inscription. Can't you remember?"

I could recall no mention of earthquakes in the inscription. The monk then produced the copy from his satchel and said triumphantly, "Now the last shred of doubt is gone, Bibhuti Babu. We have reached the correct spot. Listen to this." He read out the text in the original Prakrit: "It is related that giants from the country of the Asuras built it in the time of the Emperor Asoka in the *tremulous nether region* of the Himalayas."

Then I remembered. I had taken the phrase "tremulous nether region" to be meaningless verbiage. Not for a minute had I dreamed it might refer to a land of earthquakes. "Yes," I said, "you have caught it rightly. I had not noticed the words. Like Shillong, this place, too, is perhaps a region of earthquakes."

Suddenly I was struck by a remarkable change that had come over the headman. He was temendously excited. His tiny almond eyes were glittering brightly. His lips were parted in an effort to speak. He amazed us by reciting in pure Prakrit. "Listen ye, when the sun enters the second quarter of Sagittarius, sunlight will enter the vent in the Buddha-column and light up the divine image of the Lord, and the door of the column will magically open. This will happen for three consecutive days and then the door will close for a year. O devout monk, if you wish to make the path of Nirvana easier by gazing at the wonderful countenance of the Buddha, remember this." Having uttered all this in one breath, the headman began to pant.

In sharp surprise, the Bhikshu asked, "You—you know Prakrit?" The headman did not understand and shook his head. The help of the Bhutiya guide was sought, and through him the headman conveyed that what he had recited was their tribal mantra; through generations they learned it by heart but did not know what it meant. Hearing the verse read by the Bhikshu, the verses had come to his mind.

We exchanged glances. The Bhikshu told the headman, "Please repeat your mantra once more." He did so more slowly this time. I understood it completely. This was no mantra but the directions to enter the column. For three days in the year the heat of the sun's rays entered the column through a hole and probably warmed some mechanism. As a result, a mechanically controlled door opened. I remembered having read that in ancient Egypt and Assyria fraudulent priests had temple doors opened by such means to impress the people. The builders of this column were Asuras, that is, Assyrian sculptors. The control of its door by a similar mechanism was thus not impossible. The monks who had come with the Buddha image, surely they knew this mystery and had composed the mantra to guide future generations. But how did the headman know it?

I took a good look at his face. Though it was mainly Mongolian, the nose, the brows, and the chin suggested Aryan blood. The monks had not been able to return and the headman was a descendant of one of them. He had forgotten the history of his ancestors but had learned by heart their tribal mantra.

I collected my thoughts. The column opened for only three days in the year. Which were those three days? How long would we have to wait? I asked the Bhikshu, "When will the sun enter the second quarter of Sagittarius?" He produced an almanac from his satchel and studied it with deep concentration. After about a quarter of an hour, he raised his head. His lips were trembling and tears swam in his eyes. "Tomorrow", he said, "is the first of Magh and the sun enters the second quarter of Sagittarius." "What a strange coincidence! Suppose we had arrived three days later?" His voice shook uncontrollably. Falteringly and choked in tears, he murmured, "O Lord Buddha."

Shivers ran down my spine also. Silently I prayed, "O Lord Buddha, let not thy monk's wish be in vain."

IV

E A R L Y next morning we set out for the column. The headman accompanied us of his own will. Just outside the village, the mountain rose in very nearly sheer steps. The ascent was at times so steep that we had to climb on hand and foot. At every step, we feared we would lose our foothold and tumble down. The monk was silent, but his frail body did not lack strength. He led the way and we somehow followed. It seemed as if he was dragging us along by the power of his enthusiasm.

Yet we had to rest twice on the way. I carried a pair of binoculars and trained it on the surrounding country. Far below, the village looked toy-like and tiny. All around were lifeless, lonely mountains. At last, after struggling for more than five hours, we reached our destination. A muffled booming had for some time been reaching our ears, like drum-beats in the distance. The headman explained it was the sound of the waterfall.

When we stood at the edge of the torrent, we were struck speechless by the scene. Some fifty feet below us the river leaped into space in a welter of foam and spray. Hurtling two hundred feet in rainbow-arched descent, it stirred up a fierce whirlpool and rushed on. The spray rose to our faces like steam from a boiling cauldron.

The gorge was about fifty yards wide between the two banks. It seemed the mountains had split to make way for the imprisoned river. Two iron chains—one above, the other below —stretched from bank to bank. This was the frail bridge man had built to cross the chasm. Against the background of the thundering waterfall, the thin, rusty chains looked more fragile than a cobweb. Any strong wind, it seemed, would cleave them in two.

The scene on the other side was completely different. It seemed nature had separated the two banks because of their marked difference. The bank across seemed full of innumerable marble mounds. As far as the eye could reach, the landscape was dotted with white marble hillocks, big, small, and medium-sized. Those who have seen the Dhamma Stupa at Sarnath can somewhat visualise the scene. Behind these natural stupas, just on the edge of the deep gorge, a beautiful column rose upward like a minaret. Its stone surface sparkled in the rays of the midday sun. One felt a super-human architect alone could build such a marvellous column. It looked a creation of the world's childhood days. Human artists had also perhaps had a hand, but even careful examination through the binoculars revealed no trace of human handiwork. It was impossible to make out from the outside that the column was hollow; only at the summit I noticed a tiny opening; it was rectangular, perhaps no more than a foot in length and in breadth. This surely was the vent mentioned in the mantra.

Absorbedly, I was watching the scene. Glancing beside me, I saw the Bhikshu flat on the ground prostrating himself before the divine column.

Bhikshu Aviram did not heed our warning. He crossed along the chain bridge alone to the other side while we three watched. At every step it seemed the chain would snap, but the monk was frail and light and the chain held. Reaching the other side, he waved reassuringly to us and went toward the column. Circling it, once again he raised his hand and shouted, but the words were lost in the roar of the waterfall. It seemed he had found the door open.

He then vanished behind the column and I could see him no more. I waited with eyes glued to my binoculars. In my mind's eye, I could see the monk slowly climbing the dark

circular stairway, his trembling lips uttering indistinctly the
prayer, "Lord, lead us from darkness into light."

Did that sandalwood image still exist? Would the monk
see it? I would not, but for that I had no regrets. If the image
existed, I would have it recovered later. There would surely
be a wave of excitement throughout the country.

Ten minutes passed in such thoughts. Then everything turned
upside down. It was as if the Himalayas had suddenly gone
insane. The earth swayed, and there came from its depths a
tortured moan. It could have been the agonised cry of a mor-
tally wounded giant. The chain bridge snapped and fell into
the roaring waters.

I shall describe no more that earthquake of the first of
Magh. Only this much I shall say. Those who experienced it
in the plains of India cannot even imagine the intensity at
its epicentre.

Why we did not perish I do not know. Perhaps because our
days had not run out. I lay flat on the rocking earth. Before
my eyes the column swayed like the mast of a storm-tossed
vessel, and I gazed at it, paralysed.

Then a sick apprehension overwhelmed me. The monk—
what will happen to the monk? The intensity of the earthquake abated a little, and it seemed as if it might stop. The
binoculars were still clasped in my hand, and I lifted them
to my eyes. To attempt escape was useless. I did not even
try. The earthquake re-started with redoubled force, as if it
repented its momentary weakness and was determined not
to stop till it had destroyed the earth. But the monk? Up to
now the column was swaying like a mast. It could bear no
more and snapped in two near the base. For a second, it rocked
on the edge of the bottomless abyss and then plunged over
the precipice. A cloud of steam rose from the deep ravine and
hid it from my eyes.

While it swayed uncertainly on the edge of the abyss, I had
a fleeting glimpse of the monk. I saw him standing near the
vent, the sunlight on his face—a face illuminated with ineffable

happiness. He seemed quite unconscious of the cataclysmic events round him. The column plunged into the ravine. I saw him no more.

I RETURNED home alone. Years passed, but I could not relate the story to anyone. The thought of the Bhikshu would fill me with intense pain.

Yet I find solace in the thought that the supreme desire of his life had not remained unfulfilled. What wonderful image of the Lord he saw inside the column, I do not know. But there is no doubt that his lifelong search had not been in vain. The translucent joy in his face at the moment of death is still vivid before my eyes.

TARASANKAR BANERJEE

The Seat of Stone

I

Mining Engineer Amal said :

The story of the Mahabharat is like nectar. But I am not
talking of that Mahabharat or Greater India now. I am talking
of the new Bharat, the new India which has rebuilt the broken
temple of Somnath on the one hand, and set up the Damodar
Valley Corporation on the other.

This made me smile.

Amal said, I see you are laughing up your sleeve, but first
listen to me, and then smile, if you will. Everything has two
sides, good and bad, and I fear that if the Damodar is dammed,
and then the other rivers in the area, the pressure of water
on the mines may increase and make many of them useless.
I was moving about and collecting data on this very point.
They pay me well, but believe me I do not work for pay alone.
Call me a slave. I am possessed by a passion for inquiry.

I had a jeep and trailer that carried me, my three attendants, and all the necessary equipment wherever I wanted
to go. One day, as luck would have it, the jeep overturned.
We were all thrown out. The driver, one attendant, and I
escaped with a few scratches, but the other two attendants
were seriously hurt. The jeep was righted, but would not move.
Something had gone wrong.

This happened in an Adivasi[1] area. It was a hilly place with

---

[1] Adivasis—literally original inhabitants—are the descendants of those
people who ran away to the hills and forests when the Aryan invaders
defeated them in prehistoric times.

forests on three sides. The forest had thinned out in this particular spot with only a few scattered Sal, Mahua, and Flame
of the Forest trees. There were hillocks all around with slopes
in between. Water flowed through them in many tiny streams
and rivulets and finally mingled with the Damodar or its
tributaries.

The really thick forest was probably ten miles away. After
a good deal of thought, I decided to get the jeep pushed back
four miles or so where the injured could be attended to and
the jeep repaired by the driver. I would in the meantime go
ahead and collect as much data as possible. You know I often
wander about on foot. From war disposals goods I had collected
twenty-five knapsacks of different varieties for such tramps.
I slung one of these on my shoulders and hung a small bedding
under my armpit. Under my coat I fastened a belt with a
pistol, some bullets, and a dagger.

It was lovely country, rounded with forests and dotted with
hills. Small huts raised their heads wherever the forest was
thin. As civilisation advanced, the primitive people retreated
and they have been living, ever since, fenced in by forests.
But this region appeared to be in some ways unique. It seemed
isolated from the whole world.

The villages were small and the huts tiny, inhabited by
people ebony in complexion and rough of manner. In their
food and clothing, there was much that was barbarous by our
standards. The rooms were small and without ventilation and
therefore unhealthy. The huts however were very clean. The
frame of sal and bamboo on the mud walls and the roof of
straw were inexpensive but pretty. The plastered walls shed a
pleasing and mellow loveliness all around. Wavy lines drawn
with deft fingers on the lower walls conveyed the idea of a
billowy river. Above were trees resembling date palms and
imparting a sylvan background to the scene.

The simple nature and strong muscles of the people even in
these disease-ridden days of 'controls' seemed to reflect the
nature of the rocky soil. They felled trees in the forests and

sold them; pieced together sal leaves, caught peafowl, and
tilled the lower portion of the eroded land. In other areas,
such people go to the coal-mines, but here they did not. There
was a strong earthy smell about these men. Their minds were
as simple and generous as the plains and as soft as the grass
on virgin land.

And here lay the danger. The land that has not been tilled
may have, under the cover of grass, if not quicksands, at least
treacherous slime, causing the feet to slip. There may also be
fissures under the grass which hide reptiles. That is why I
was cautious in approaching these people. I had no evil thought;
I only wanted to avoid treading on any delicate spot or offen-
ding them inadvertently by my speech. I knew their dialect
well and used it with care.

One day——

Amal drew himself up, pulled vainly at his cigar and went on:
It was dusk when I came to the village. A little way off,
there was a small hill. I saw in my map that there was an
abandoned pit on the other side. I decided that I would proceed
along the line of that pit and cross the hill to reach the
Damodar Valley Project area. I had instructed my driver to
take the jeep there by the circuitous macadam road and wait
for me there. I looked at the hill again. The stones of a lower
stratum had been pushed through as a result of a prehistoric
earthquake. Beyond it was the abandoned pit and further
away another pit which was still in use. I had intended to
reach the latter before nightfall so that I might secure food
and shelter. But night came while I was on the way. There
was the danger of wild animals, besides there was that abandoned pit. Who knows what sort of abyss it might lead one
to? I therefore stopped when I came to the village.

It was a small Adivasi village. I could not get a clear and
distinct view in the dark but it seemed that it was somehow
different. The drawings on the walls were highly artistic.

Some huts had toys and pots of clay in the yard. I saw potter's wheels too. Are these people not Adivasis? I wondered. I did not pursue the thought, for the question of shelter was important. I knew from experience that it was hardly the thing to ask men—men who could not keep pace with the evolution of society—about their caste and profession. Such questions from a stranger of the upper class would create misgivings in their minds and they would feel they were being slighted.

I approached the headman of the village and asked for shelter. He complied with alacrity. Even his cordiality somehow appeared distinctive. Right in front of his hut was a shed, neat and somewhat different. The ceiling was made of sal wood, with crossbeams on all sides; the uprights were also made of sal and the door of bamboo. The floor was plastered clean with a mixture of mud and cowdung. These people offered me that shed. It was the guest house, village council hall and temple yard—all in one. A big lamp of mahua oil was lighted for me. The floor which was clean already was swept cleaner. Then the headman put his hand on the cleaned spot and said, "Mr. Guest, take your seat here and stay," in other words, "Please sit down." He brought me thick boiled buffalo milk, gur, and rice crispies. With folded hands he said: "Mr. Guest, the land has stolen sugar and we do not eat it either. Could you manage with gur?"

Then we started talking. I soon found that I was right: these people were different from the Adivasis of other villages. They made toys and vessels of clay and did carpentry. They were potters as well as carpenters. They tilled the land also. This had been a village of artists and artisans for ages. As they say in Sanskrit, "since the birth of the sun, the moon and the earth." Any other profession was forbidden them.

Then the headman asked, "Mr. Guest, where will you go through the hills and the jungles?" I began to give the usual explanation and told him about the Damodar Valley Project. The wild Damodar would be tamed. He listened with attention and heaved a deep sigh, "O Lord I bow to thee again and again."

I was struck by his posture: he had been squatting with his elbows on his knees; his gaze was fixed on the ground. He was listening to me intently and perhaps trying to visualise what I said. He raised his face to offer his salutation and then, looking toward the village path called out, "Who is there? Who is standing there?"

Somebody indeed was standing there. The reply came: "It is me." "Is that Kandan? When did you come back?" the headman asked.

"Just now. I have not yet been to my hut," replied the other.

"Not yet? Then what are you doing standing there?"

"I was looking at him. Who is he?"

"Oh, he is the guest! Come in. Sit down. How are you?"

"I am all right."

The man came forward. The light was dim and I had glasses which reflect the light. I could not see him distinctly. He looked tall and strong.

The headman said, "Mr. Guest, this man is my son-in-law. He will understand better what you have said. He works in bungalows, has seen towns, travelled in trains and seen life. I ask him not to. One should not disobey the commands of the gods but he does not listen. What can I do ?"

Kandan—for that was how he was addressed by the headman—left. "I am leaving Sir," he said.

"You see what I mean," said the headman. "My daughter is a good girl but this is her fate. What can I do if her husband will not obey the commands of the gods?"

Next morning, as I hung up my many-chambered knapsack and put on my pistol belt, I toyed with the idea of staying for another day. The work on the crossbeams and the ceiling surprised me. What astonished me most was that the crossbeams were full of carvings, but none of them was of leaves or creepers, flowers or birds or beasts; they were all of human faces. There were rows of them and they were all of the same mould. Perhaps the artists here had learned to draw only one kind of face. But I changed my mind and decided regretfully to go. There was no time. The headman was standing there. I asked leave of him and got out. He came as far as the boundary of the village, knelt down and said with folded hands, "Mr. Guest, forgive us if we have been guilty of any lapse." He stood up and remained standing.

Outside the village stretched the fields and the hill and there suddenly—

Amal Chaudhury must have had a vision of what he was going to describe. There came a sudden change in him; in his features, voice, gestures. He sat up erect. The slight inclination of his neck and his leisurely, cultivated pose vanished. So did the pretension of detachment in his tone. His eyes glittered. He sat upright and, with a fixed stare, blurted out,

I was suddenly attacked. I had left the village behind and moved on. I came to a small hill stream by a boulder. A tall black shape suddenly appeared from behind and stood in my way. It seemed that he had burst out of the boulder.

I was startled and came to a halt. His eyes flashed black hatred. In a fierce but muffled voice he snarled at me with bared teeth.

My hand moved toward my belt, but the man was too quick. He grasped it and said, "I know you have a gun there."

He appeared to know me but I could not place him. I am not a coward; but I was handicapped by the knapsack on my back. I restrained myself and said, "What do you want? Money?"

He replied, "Don't you remember me?" His teeth seemed to protrude still further. He continued: "I recognised you as soon as I set eyes on you last evening. I did not have a wink of sleep the whole night. The old headman was there, otherwise I would have settled old scores there and then. I have been waiting outside the village since dawn. Come now, lead the way. Kandan will settle accounts. Yes, tell me how you like it now."

I was not overmuch afraid but I did feel a little uneasy. What puzzled me was his talk about settling accounts.

Kandan said, "So, you have not recognised me yet. Look at this." He pushed aside his long hair and pointed to a big scar on his forehead.

"Don't you remember this scar? No?"

A cruel smile spread over his face.

In a flash, the incident came back to me. I saw again the railway platform, and a tall, black vigorous youth running with an iron rod in his hand. A party of well-dressed men pursued him with cries of "Catch hold of him! Catch hold of him!"

That man with the iron rod was Kandan. I had flung a stone at him and caused that wound on his forehead. Stunned by the blow, the rod had dropped from his hand. He slumped down and clasped at his head. He was a man who had gone about in cities, worked in collieries and been quite conscious of his rights. He had been lying on a bench in the third class waiting room. A Bengali gentleman travelling with his wife had demanded that bench and asked him to sleep on the floor. Kandan had replied: "You go and sleep on the floor yourself."

"Look at the impertinence of the fellow!" the gentleman had exclaimed.

"Don't abuse me, I say."

"What nonsense! How have I abused you?"

"Who are you to call me fellow?"

The gentleman was indeed wrong. Hitherto we have bossed over these men and claimed to civilise them. Now things have changed and they would not stand any patronising.

That was how the quarrel had started. Kandan had his ticket in his pouch and felt he had as much right to sit on the bench as the gentleman. He argued like a lawyer but others took the side of the gentleman. A few supported Kandan at first but, when he ignored the claims of a lady, he lost their sympathy.

He had laid himself full length on the bench; now he sat up and said, "All right, let them sit."

"You get up first, how else will they sit?"

"No, no. Let them sit by my side. First that little girl and then let the mother sit by her on the other side. I won't get up. No!"

Kandan won the bout. The little girl sat next to him and then the lady. The gentleman had no place on the bench. He sat for a while in the tea stall and then started walking up and down. It was getting into the early hours of dawn when one feels sleepiest. Kandan must have dozed and knocked against the little girl. The gentleman who had been fuming all the while rushed up and slapped Kandan hard. Kandan was wild and returned a heartier smack on the gentleman's cheek. A hue and cry was raised and men rushed on Kandan and started hitting him. All the gentlemen were agreed that men like Kandan had become too impertinent and deserved a lesson.

Kandan tried to return the compliment and delivered a few blows. But how long can one man fight so many ? He tried to escape but could not. In desperation Kandan picked up a broken iron rail and, brandishing it, he was running away. That is indeed how a frightened barbarian would run away. I was coming to the platform from the opposite end. On hearing the shouts and seeing a tall black man running with an iron rod in his hand, I naturally took him for a criminal. I had a pistol in my belt but I did not fire. I picked up a stone and threw it at him. Since childhood I have never hit any target with a stone. But perhaps because it was fate, the stone struck him right on the forehead. If he were stationary, perhaps there would have been no damage. But the momentum of the opposing forces made it a more serious affair. The fellow dropped the iron rod and slumped down. Before I could say anything, the crowd was on him. I was full of remorse but I could give him no protection. I rushed for the police and Kandan was saved by their intervention. I learned that the 'assaulted' lady's age was nine and the outrage consisted in dozing and brushing against her. My regrets knew no bounds. His deep black forehead painted with the deep red dye of blood, his body sore and stiff with beating, Kandan looked on with listless eyes at the roof of the Police Station; perhaps he wanted to see the sky.

It was I who had asked the Police to send him to the hospital. The doctor was known to me. I wrote to him to give him an injection and requested him to treat the patient with special care. These people of the forest have enormous endurance, but I wanted to treat him as an equal. If you say that not a philosophical impulse but the pricks of conscience made me so act, I won't object.

So this was my man—this Kandan. I had totally forgotten him. Perhaps the secret consciousness of guilt had drawn a veil on my memory but the veil dropped as soon as I saw the scar. In a flash I recollected everything.

Kandan held my hand in an iron grip. The veins in his long, black hand stood out under the pressure. His muscles swelled, his eyes grew red and his nostrils swelled. On his forehead stood out three veins like the sign of a trident. I was on my guard now. A barbarian's love is as strong as his hate. Concentrating all the force of my personality, I said: "Let go my hand."

The mask of culture dropped from me. In spite of my effort at dignity, my voice was high and excited. I knew I had done him wrong, I could not accept him as a judge. On the contrary, I looked on him as an enemy. If only I could get at my pistol, I would not hesitate to fire. In a high and excited voice I repeated: "Let go my hand, I say."

Kandan burst out, "No!"

It was broken country full of forests and hills. His "No" echoed and re-echoed all around. Perhaps the spot where we stood was a centre of such echoes.

In a harsh but muffled voice he said: "You struck me with a stone. I will pay you back in the same coin." He had in his left hand a sharp-pointed stone weighing more than a pound.

Suddenly from the top of the hill behind came a high frightened voice, "Kandan."

I realised that it was the voice of the headman. Again the voice cried, "Kandan."

Kandan was startled by the first cry. Now he turned his eyes from me and looked at the hill. He continued to gaze as though he was transfixed. Fear wrought changes like a kaleidoscope on his face. Have you seen the covering of ash on a glowing ember? The ash falls off, the wind sweeps it away, the ember glows sharp and bright again and again the ash settles on it. It was exactly the same on his face.

Yes, it was indeed the headman.

He rushed toward us. He was gasping. His eyes were full of panic but were also full of an expression of authority and stern rebuke. He gasped, "Let go the guest's hand."

Like a snake whose fangs have been taken out, Kandan hissed, "No, no, I won't let him go."

"Let him go, I say," repeated the headman. "Look at the stone on the hill," he commanded.

Kandan started.

As if he was chanting a hymn, the headman said in his dialect: "Look at that white stone there. Keep looking. The white stone has turned black, the blue of the sky will presently turn into copper, the smell of burning bodies will foul the air; the river water will swarm with insects; caterpillars will settle on the leaves and flowers; the birds will shriek like vultures; the bamboo pipe will be dumb and the golden colour of the sun-god will turn into lead, there will be darkness. The world will be turned into darkness—!"

Kandan interrupted him, "No, No! Say no more, please."

Kandan let go my hand. What was more, I saw the fire in him had gone out. He looked like a burned out ember.

The headman ordered, "Come now, hold the hand of the guest and ask his forgiveness."

Kandan knelt down and with folded hands said: "I place the sin of my heart at your feet. Tread on it, destroy it, and redeem me. Come to my house and accept the honey of my mind."

The headman said to me: "You must stay one day more, Mr. Guest, and eat in Kandan's house. If you refuse, Kandan will go to hell and the whole village will be ruined. The white stone there—on the top of the hill—will turn black and then the blue of the sky will be copper. The smell of dead bodies will foul the air."

The headman went on, "The river will swarm with worms; caterpillars will settle on the leaves and flowers; the birds will shriek like vultures; the bamboo pipe will be dumb and then the sun . . . the glorious god of shining gold will turn into a dark lump of lead."

He was speaking as if he was chanting a hymn. I am no believer, but I was touched by his deep faith. His voice trembled with emotion and I could not say no.

II

T H E   M I L K in Kandan's house was boiled thick. With honey collected from the forests, a rice pudding was made and served to me.

Dark but quiet and lovely was Kandan's wife, the headman's daughter. Her big, innocent eyes were full of a sad resignation that moved me.

Kandan was sitting in front, still and lifeless. Everything to be done was being done by his wife. She put the dish before me and sat by the side of her husband. With folded hands, she said, "Dear Guest, please forgive our wrongs. Satisfy yourself with these sweets and the honey of our heart. Let the burning of our heart cease."

Kandan was uttering the same words, but slowly. His lips were trembling and his accents broke. His wife looked at him in surprise. The headman was also looking at him, threateningly.

I saw that Kandan could not conquer his hatred.

I said, "I accept your sincere gifts."

Milk and honey are things to relish, and I drank them as such. Otherwise these people would be ruined; Kandan would go to hell; the village would be ruined, the white stone on that hill would turn black and the soft blue of the sky would be transformed into hard copper; the air would be fouled by the smell of corpses and even the sun would die.

Gradually however my reason came back. I asked, "What does all this mean?"

They did not know what all this meant. They only knew that this was the command of the man who had founded the village. The same man had set up the white stone on the top of the hill.

The headman explained, "It is not that he left only the stone. He also installed the god. One day that god left us. Strange men came and set fire to the temple and everything was burned to ashes. No one else could make that image. Look there—."

He showed me the crossbeam on which was a series of heads. In the dark of the night, I had not seen them distinctly but in the clear daylight, I could make out details of the single type of head. It was the calm face of a man in a trance. But there was something indistinct in the images, either indistinctly carved, or time had made them so.

The headman said, "You cannot carve the image of the god unless you know him, unless you can surrender your heart's anger to the god.

"We only make toys of clay and articles of wood. We do not know the god."

I felt like saying, "There's no such thing as your god," but my tongue remained silent.

The headman continued: "This is the order of the god—if anyone in this village desires to harm a guest, he must sacrifice his violence and anger at his feet and feed him with milk and honey. He must fold his hands and ask forgiveness. If he does not do so, that white stone will turn black, and then the blue sky will become copper."

He repeated those strange words of faith as if he was chanting a hymn. He concluded: "Mr. Guest, that stone will not continue to be white for long. Men like this fellow, Kandan, are being born in large numbers now. The jewel of the day will turn into lead."

Suddenly Kandan rose and left.

I DECIDED to climb the hill and see for myself.

That hill of theirs lay on the side of the road, just beyond the village. It was not a hill but just a hillock full of boulders. Long ago, the stone layer under the earth was thrown up by an earthquake and pushed up into the sky. On top of the mass of black stone was a block of white stone. It was a seat made of a strange kind of white stone. The people of the village scrubbed it and cleaned it. No dirt could settle on it, not even moss during the rains. Constant scrubbing had smoothed it and given it a fine polish. The pile of black stones set it off.

Disappointed, I was coming down when I met a Brahmin. His face was longish, his nose aquiline and eyes curiously round. He was thin and on the crown of his bald head he wore a tuft of hair with a flower tied to the end. He had a basket of flowers in his hands. I realised that he was coming to worship.

The Brahmin was surprised to see me. He tried to guess who I was, and his round eyes shone. With a suspicious look, he asked, "Who are you, please?"

I said: "A visitor."

"A visitor to visit coal sites? But coal is below this place. This hill is mine. The coal stretches right up to its bottom. Will you buy it?"

I laughed and said: "No, I have not come to seek coal. I came to see this holy place."

"To see this holy place?" he repeated in surprise, but soon corrected himself and said, "It is a holy place, Sir. This spot

was the seat of meditation of a great saint. If you wish anything
here, you will get it. Look over there, on the farther side of the
forest you will see the Paresnath Hills, the holy peak looking
like a black cloud. This is a subsidiary shrine, subsidiary to
the holy temple of Paresnath. You will redeem your sins and
will attain eternal salvation, if......"

I interrupted him and said: "Look here, Brahmin. My sin
is black like your coal. It cannot be washed away and if you
burn it, it will only turn into ashes. In any case, I do not
want salvation. I am full of desire, but I cannot get what I
want by bowing to your god. However, if you will tell me the
story of your god, I will give you some money."

"Certainly, Sir. Let me first finish the service. It will take
only three minutes—not a minute more."

He started muttering *mantras* and dropping flowers. He
carried a pot of water also, and poured out some water and
then completed the service by bowing his head to the ground.

"Will you sit here, Sir?" he said and added,

"You must pay two rupees to the poor Brahmin."

*　　　　*　　　　*　　　　*

Amal's eyes grew dreamy. He paused for a few seconds and
continued:

Miracle of miracles! From out of a poor, cunning Brahmin,
came another man: he was the teller of mythological stories
and he narrated his story in striking language.

"Paresnath was one of the greatest teachers of the Jains.
Over there on that peak—named after him—he attained
salvation. If you touch the dust of that place, high thoughts
will come to you and you will progress toward 'salvation'.
A sanyasi built the first seat of worship for Paresnath on that
holy peak. He had a disciple who had royal blood in his
veins. The royal disciple chose this hill as the seat of his
devotion.

"This forest land—even today it is called Panch Koot—has

been the age-old abode of primitive tribes. They are simple, vigorous folk. Surrounded by hills, the forest with its gorgeous beauty lay at their feet. The Borakar and the Damodar flowed through the forest. Tigers roamed about it. Here these vigorous people lived. A prince was born to their king. The queen died and the new-born baby was handed over to a nurse.

"Some time earlier, a stranger had come to the king's court. He was able and prospered. The laws of our forefathers forbid us to give shelter, far less, indulgence to strangers. But the king ignored the Shastric injunctions and gave the stranger every encouragement. He had become the most powerful man in the state when the king lost his wife.

"The king had a loyal old minister who watched the development in helplessness. He scented danger and warned the king, but the king would pay no heed. At last, in desperation he retired and the stranger became the minister.

"It happened as the minister had feared. The stranger murdered the king and became king himself. The people of the state were distraught. On the plea of the need for more revenue, the new king converted honey into wine and made a brew out of rice. The men were fuddled with drink and the women became like courtesans.

"In those days, all women here were adept in dancing. When the dark clouds covered the skies over this forest land, the top of the sal trees used to be arched over by a thousand rainbows. The peacock on the hill was like a cloud in the sky. Clouds sailed along the sky and the dancing peacocks spread their tails above the tops of the trees. In palaces and in cottages, the women decked their hair with *kurchi* flowers and learned to dance. Even now, they dance and sing in the rains.

> *Come hither O cloud*
> *Sit awhile near the head of our land,*
> *Melt the hill with your tears,*
> *I dye my hair with your colour*
> *Dye it with care.*

"These women who had danced in their homes now degener-
ated into dancing courtesans. You have seen the Damodar
which during floods sweeps through the land. Revelry swept
the land like a flood. The new king now sought the prince's
blood. He wished to destroy the seed, but a nurse saved the
child. She took him to the old minister, who vanished with the
prince. He deposited the boy with the sanyasi on Paresnath
Hill and died the same night.

"The boy grew up under the care of the sanyasi. He used to
meditate and the boy observed him. He chanted hymns and
the boy listened: non-violence, non-anger, and truth are the
true religion, learned the boy. The sanyasi went to the holy
peak to build the temple of Paresnath. The prince was still a
boy and accompanied him. The sanyasi worked and the boy
observed and learned the technique of the art.

"When the work was complete and the sanyasi wished to
return, he called the youth and told him the secret of his life.
It made the youth's blood boil. He had a mad desire to rush
and plunge a dagger in the king's heart.

"The young prince could not however persist with the
thought of revenge. Here you see this white stone. It was the
remnant of the material which had gone into the building
of the temple. The youth had thought of using it to make a
seat for his god, but the moment he thought of revenge an
extraordinary thing happened. He felt a deep burning pain in
his head and all over his body. In a trice the white stone turned
red hot and then assumed the colour of a burned out ember.
The soft blue of the sky vanished and became as hard as copper.
The air became heavy and pungent with the smell of dead
bodies. The transparent water of the spring became discoloured and poisoned. Leaves and flowers fell from the trees.
Their beauty gone, the forest became foul with poisonous
insects. The birds screamed like vultures, the pipe in the
youth's hand burst. The sun shed its lustre and turned into
lead.

"The young prince cried and tried to recall the face of the

god whom he used to see in his dreams, but where was he ?
He saw instead a terrible figure with bloodshot eyes, sharp
claws and cruel canine teeth.

" 'Save me,' the young prince cried, and fell at the feet of
his guru.

" 'I have no power to save you. Pray instead to the god
you worship, whom you have seen in your dreams.'

" 'But I cannot recall his face. I see only a terrible face.'

" 'That is the image of violence. If you avenge your father
and become king, it will settle on your right hand which holds
the sword. Get rid of it.'

" 'How can I do so? It is standing in front of me.'

" 'Pray and meditate.'

" 'Tell me which mantra to repeat.'

"Then the sanyasi placed in his hands a clod of clay and a
piece of wood. 'It takes time to carve on stone,' he said. 'Carve
an image with this every day and try to remove the violence
from your heart. At first your images will take the horrible
shape you have seen, but gradually you will perceive a change.
As you change, this stone will also change colour. The day you
attain salvation and discard violence, you will find that the
stone has regained its stainless white glory. Then you can
instal your god on it. Now go back to that hill. This holy peak
belongs to Lord Paresnath. It is the home of bliss; you have no
right to live here any longer.'

"Sir, this is that hill. Here the youth began his strange form
of worship. There were no hymns to chant, only image after
image to carve in wood with chisel and hammer. Sometimes,
he made models in clay also. The first image was terrible and
reflected the violence in his heart. He went on carving image
after image, making model after model. Putting them side by
side he observed them.

"And every day first thing in the morning he would look
at the seat of stone.

"The men who now live in this village are natives of the
soil and kinsmen of this prince. They supplied him with food

and looked with wonder at the work of the frenzied artist.

"A time came when the images no longer held any terror, and became like those of normal men. The stone seat had also turned grey.

"A remarkable thing happened one day. The young man finished an image and looked at it with satisfaction. It had the form of a handsome prince. Just then sounds of horses' hoofs reached his ears. A messenger appeared and told him that the king of the land had heard of his skill and wanted him to carve an image of the prince.

"The artist did not look up. He merely said, 'No, I won't go.'

" 'He will give you ample reward,' the messenger said.

" 'No,' the artist replied.

"The messenger left and the artist's eyes followed him as he rode back. He felt a great satisfaction in his mind. He had sent away the messenger—the messenger of *that* king.

"Next morning he gave a suppressed cry when he came near the seat. The grey had grown a shade darker.

"Presently, he took some clay and started modelling it. The image showed traces of the former cruelty.

"He looked at the sky. There was a shade of copper in it and the air was again heavy. A pyre seemed to be burning somewhere far away.

" 'O Lord! O my Guru! What is all this? Save me O Lord, save me!'

"Again, the sound of horses' hoofs came to his ears. It was another official sent by the king.

" 'No! No! No!' said the artist. With folded hands I pray to you. Let me alone. Do not disturb my meditations. I won't go, I won't!'

"The official left.

"The artist felt reassured. So, he had not lost his resolve. Again he started modelling. But this time the model became still more fearful. The colour of the stone became darker.

" 'Good Lord! Is it then—?'

"He began to reflect and spent the whole night in reflection.

"The morning came and he heard a wail in the forest. The whole world appeared to be mourning. He felt it was his heart which wailed, but it was not. It was the lamentation of a woman.

"The sound of lamentation came nearer. It was a middle-aged woman—a mother.

"He asked, 'Who may you be, mother?'

" 'I? Have pity on me, artist. My son, the prince—'

"Suddenly she stopped, stared in amazement for a moment, and then rushed to the wooden image and took it in her arms. It was the image of the beautiful prince which the artist had carved.

" 'Here he is! This is my son, the prince,' she said.

"The woman was the queen. Her son was dying, and the king had sent for the artist to draw a likeness of the dying boy. But the artist had refused and derived satisfaction from his denial. Now the queen had come to ask him to carve an image of the boy, for how could she live in the house without him?

" 'O artist, are you omniscient? Are you a god? You have already made the image of the healthy prince for the bereaved mother. Give it to me, please. Tell me what is your price?'

"The artist felt as if the sky was filled with nectar. The air was thick with the smell of honey, the birds were singing and the strains of the pipe were spreading all over the world. The sal tree was decked with flowers.

"Tears streamed out of his eyes and fell on that seat of stone. He said, 'Take it mother and forgive me.'

"The queen did not answer him. She said instead in wonder, 'Are you really omniscient?'

"She pointed to the terrible image and said, 'This indeed is my husband's likeness. A skin disease has made him look horrible. He is exactly like this.'

" 'You may take this image too. I pray to God, may your son live and your husband recover. But you are tired. Have some food.'

"He gave her milk and honey.

"The queen left. Now the artist, with his heart full, took a piece of wood and sat near the stone.

"The seat had turned spotless white. On it fell the glow of the sun."

III

With his eyes closed, Amal sat silent for a while. Soon he resumed but with eyes still closed.

When the Brahmin finished his story I was overwhelmed and sat still. The time, the surroundings and the mood mingled to give me a strange feeling of serenity. The sal forest on all sides shone in the noon-day sun. The deep blue of the hills on the far horizon, the silence, broken only by the chirping of the birds, and that white seat of stone in front—this was the background against which the Brahmin had told me his strange story.

The spell of the trance was broken by the Brahmin.

The strange story-teller was suddenly transformed into a shrewd man of the world. He put out his hand and the gesture of begging could not be mistaken.

His narrative had charmed me. I gave him a five-rupee note. It made him voluble. He repeatedly blessed me and then immediately sought my advice on a question of law. A British company had taken a lease of an adjoining piece of land from him. Now the company had closed the pit and left. They did not pay him even the minimum royalty now. He added that the company had taken out, without prior agreement, earth from this hill and compensation was also due on that score. He had gone or would shortly go to a court of law.

I gave him what advice I could, and the Brahmin left. Nearly three-quarters of the day had gone. Evening was spreading over the forest land: there was a trace of yellow in the sunshine.

The birds chirped. Their mid-day rest over, they took to the sky in flocks. I heard some peacocks too. I sat on. I had forgotten my journey altogether. After a while I got up and looked for an image carved in wood. I knew for certain that I should not find any. The place had been ravaged by time and men. The only thing that remained was that seat of stone. They had broken the last image the artist had carved, set fire to the temple and left without looking at the seat. Only that white seat remained on top of the black hill. So I found nothing. I sat for long and mused. I recalled the row of carved heads on the crossbeam of that shed. They were the history behind the Brahmin's story.

The sun dropped lower in the western sky. The evening rays fell on the sal, mahua and flame of the forest trees. A strange beauty settled on the thick forest toward the east. The birds flocked to their nests in the wood. I also got up. I had to go. On the other side, beyond that abandoned pit, I would pitch my camp. As I got up I noticed a lone woman with downcast eyes climbing slowly. She was too tired or too sad to walk faster.

Perhaps she was coming to light the evening lamp. She must be a daughter of the village. Next moment I recognised her. She was Kandan's wife, the daughter of the headman. She came up and started when she saw me. A picture of sadness, she fixed her eyes on me.

I said, "I have come to visit the seat of your god."

She stood, with that silent look in her eyes.

"I am going," I said, "You have come to light the lamp, haven't you?"

She said: "No, sir!" She paused for a while and added: "My husband has run away."

"Run away! You mean Kandan has run away?"

"Yes, sir. He does not share our faith. Dear guest, don't go that way tonight, if he is lying in wait, then—"

She trembled.

If Kandan did me harm, then that white stone would turn black; the soft blue of the sky would be hard like copper; the air would be heavy with foul smell and the sun would turn into lead.

I looked at her in wonder and amazement, but she did not feel shy.

She was dark and yet what sweetness in her eyes and grace and loveliness in her face! The lips were thin and black, but her smile soothed the mind. Suddenly tears rolled down her cheeks. She wiped them quickly and said: "Dear guest, you are a god to us. You bless him so that he may turn over a new leaf. I married him against my father's wishes. The whole village was against him; but I listened to none. Why has he changed ? The men of the village say, my father says, he is doomed to go to hell. How can I stand that ?"

She began by speaking to me, but as she went on, she forgot me and addressed the Seat of Stone. She knelt before the stone and folded her hands, her lips trembling and tears streaming down her face. She remained thus for some time and then placed her head against the stone. Never before had I seen such self-surrender. She was sobbing and my heart was filled with pity, but I could stay there no more. I felt I should not stay. I had no right to.

I started to descend. When I reached the bottom, I heard her voice, "Dear guest!"

I looked back. She was standing there looking extremely worried. She was calling me. I shouted, "Don't fear, I shall pass through safely."

She continued to stand there. I took out the pistol and held it in my hand. You never can tell. But I decided I would not kill Kandan. If it was necessary, I might only wound him.

I took the same path as before. I wanted to see if Kandan had returned. I had a desire also to conciliate him by paying him some money. Besides, I did not like to take the other path. Indeed, as I reached my destination, the area of the Damodar Valley Project, I had to submit to a search of my belongings. Think of the trouble—the 48-chambered knapsack and, on top of it all, the pistol, the dagger and the bullets!

No doubt I had a licence, a letter of introduction and my mining engineer's certificate, but the police would not let me pass easily. To prove that I was not a criminal would require the sending of four or five telegrams. But I was lucky, I met a friend among the police officers, Makhan Babu, the I. B. Inspector. He was a cultured man, an M. A. in Bengali literature and a stage-fan. He was also somewhat eccentric. He was the officer-in-charge at the advance outpost. He saved me the trouble of unloosening the strap. On hearing my story he said, "Don't take this road. The Intelligence Branch police of two States, West Bengal and Bihar, have gathered together. Something is up. Ask no questions, for I cannot answer you. I shall send for your jeep. Go back the way you came, and the sooner the better. It is a big affair."

I started as soon as the jeep came.

Makhan Babu said, "It is better to go back the way you came. Good luck!"

Once cloth is torn, you are not safe even if you stitch it. It may give way in another place. It is the same with a car. Once it gives trouble, it will go out of order again. My jeep had been repaired out of town, and it had run 50 miles. It now stopped suddenly. At sundown, I entered the forest. The pit still in use was behind me. Before me was the abandoned pit bordering on the Brahmin's property. Beyond was that hillock with the stone seat at the top. I had intended to cross the hillock and the forest behind it. There was the village, but this time I need not accept anybody's hospitality. I had my men with me, and the tent. We had enough food with us. Next morning I would call on the headman, gather news of Kandan and give him some money.

Amal stopped and added with a smile,

The idea was foolish, but the thought came to me that I would strike my forehead with a stone till it bled. This would lessen the violence in Kandan's heart. He would get no peace except through an act forbidden to him. I would in a different way fulfil the desire.

But the jeep failed on the way. The forest was not altogether thin. Sal, flame of the forest and mahua trees had grown thick. There were bushes of thorn and kurchi. We pushed the jeep away from the road-side and pitched our camp.

It was a bright night. The moon was eleven or twelve days old. The sky was deep blue. The moonlight found chinks in the foliage and lighted the leafy forest. It was a wonderful sight. As I walked, the moonbeams appeared like jewels scattered in the forest. The story of the *Ramayana* came to my mind—Ravana kidnapped Sita and she threw down her jewellery from the sky. Some of it fell on the ground and some got stuck in the branches and leaves of big trees. The forest was calm, only countless insects, myriads and myriads of them, were droning. An orchestra of insects! I had a desire to see the moon in the open sky. With slow steps I advanced.

I had reached almost the end of the forest when I heard human voices. I halted and tried to see. Before I could see them, I realised they were lovers meeting in the forest. I could hear two voices distinctly, but could not catch the words of the woman, spoken in a low sweet voice. Next moment I heard the man's voice.

"No, no, no. Kandan won't go. He does not believe in all this. He won't crawl from the village up to the hill. He won't ask forgiveness of the whole village with folded hands. I won't obey your father, I won't."

"If you do not obey my father, at least obey the god!"

"No, no, how many times shall I tell you! I don't believe in this stone. I'll spill that man's blood. I'll show them that the stone doesn't turn black, that nothing happens. I'll...."

"No, no, please don't say that, I beg of you with bended knees."

"Listen, if you love me, come away tomorrow night. I'll take you away. If you don't come, let it be. Kandan won't come back. He sticks to his word."

So, it was Kandan and his wife.

He would not obey the rules and traditions of his people.

He had to ask forgiveness from door to door, prostrate himself and crawl along the ground from the village up to the seat of stone on the hill. With him his wife had to come with a vessel full of water on her head. With that water he had to wash the stone, ask forgiveness and say, "Forgive me, forgive my sin. Remain white and spotless." Again he must come back crawling. With him must come the whole village, men, women and children, shouting in a chorus, "Oh, Lord! Forgive the sinner." Kandan would not accept such humiliation and insult. He would leave the village instead.

"What do you say? Speak! Shall I come tomorrow night and wait?"

"I will come. Tell me who is dearer to me than you?"

I was reflecting whether I should go forward or not. My remorse knew no bounds. I decided to move forward and ask Kandan's forgiveness. I felt like saying, "Strike me, Kandan, but have peace of mind."

Before I could do anything, there was a sound of cars—heavy vehicles, not my jeep: the continuous groan of powerful engines echoed through the forest. Not one, but two, three four cars. What's the matter, so many motor-cars at this time of the night?

I heard Kandan's voice, "Run back, run home. It is the police! Run away."

I heard the rushing of footsteps. I could see now that Kandan, tall and black, was running away fast from the cover of a bush of kurchi. Like a tiger of the forest, he flitted through the trees and vanished.

The girl got up from behind the bush and wended her way through the trees with tired footsteps. She paused at intervals, trying to see Kandan. I could understand her suspense.

The police! But why did Kandan run away? Then I remembered with a start what the Inspector, Makhan Babu, had said.

The police jeeps were hooting. I rushed back and saw that my fears were well founded. Our camp was surrounded by the police. I had with me the pistol, the dagger and the bullets.

I emptied my pockets and started to show them my papers, my letters of introduction, permits issued by the Mining Federation and the Government of India with my photo on them. Makhan Babu reached the spot. He smiled and said: "What's wrong now?"

I answered, "The jeep is out of order."

As we were talking, two more truck-loads of policemen appeared. The officer who was examining my papers smiled and said, "Don't go any further. Be on your guard. Makhan Babu will stay here."

I realised that though he believed me, he yet set a guard on me. My jeep was out of order. I could not move. It was nearing dawn. But did Kandan belong to a gang of dacoits? There were big gangs in this locality. They raided and looted business establishments. But Makhan Babu—

Suddenly, the sound of a shot was heard.

Makhan Babu said, "The raid has begun."

At dawn, the forest resounded with reports of guns. The sounds echoed far from hillock to hillock.

Makhan Babu said, "When World War II ended, the Allies had made stockpiles of deadly weapons. A party of revolutionaries stole a number of weapons and explosives and concealed them somewhere here underground, in a pit. Last evening one of them was arrested and he confessed that a man of this locality, called Kandan, had been put on guard over the abandoned pit."

So, it was toward that pit that Kandan had rushed back.

Suddenly, there was the sound of an explosion. It was a tremendous, terrible sound. Our ear-drums seemed to burst. The trees were trembling like leaves. The earth was shaken, too. Dust obscured the view. The tremendous force of the explosion raised earth, stone, and dust high into the sky.

We sat down.

It was Makhan Babu who spoke first. "Capture has not been possible. They have exploded everything. That fellow Kandan used to do explosive work in a colliery."

Makhan Babu wanted to move forward. He said to me, "Come with me. We must go ahead."

His jeep turned toward the edge of the forest beyond which was the hillock with the stone seat. As we came near the hillock, we saw the police at the top.

Again, another sound came. It was not the sound of an explosion. It was a groan. Have you heard the groaning of the earth during an earthquake? It was the same kind of long-drawn groan. The trees were shaking, the earth was trembling.

I shouted to the driver, "Stop."

The man was afraid. He stopped.

I shouted, "Back the car."

"Why!" asked Makhan Babu? "Is it an earthquake? I say, what's that?"

"No, the earth is subsiding."

"What?"

"The pit is subsiding. The company hollowed out the hillside and did little sand-packing. Now the hill is subsiding as a result of the explosion. It is going down. Look!"

Luckily, we were outside the danger zone. The earth was torn by fissures. Big trees began to shake. I realised that their roots were being snapped like the cables of a ship in a storm. They staggered and leaned on one side and then fell with a monstrous sound. The earth was subsiding. The pent-up air was gushing out. Stones were flying. It was an awful sight—a great destruction—the end of an epoch. Shiva, the god of destruction, danced. The earth subsided.

We suddenly saw the hillock tottering. Stones were falling off. The seat of stone was shaking. The hillock of that great artist was tumbling down. It sank with a tremendous noise.

What happened to the seat of stone? Did it vanish into the bowels of the earth, along the tunnel of a new age?

Will it never shine white again? Once it is black, will not the sky turn copper? Will not the smell of burned flesh foul the air? Was it lost indeed—wiped off like the time that is past?

There, standing at the edge of that sunken hillock, groups

of men and women were waiting. The old headman was beating his breast.

What's that? A young woman rushed out. She was Kandan's wife, the headman's daughter.

"Come back, O Lord! Forgive my husband's sins."

Cries were raised on all sides. But that quiet woman had gone wild. Like a frightened doe, she plunged into the debris. No one could tell when it would sink. But she did not care.

"Where's the seat, where is it?" She continued her mad search. She could not bear the complaints against her husband. Fearing eternal punishment for him, she was frantic. She could not stand her father beating his breast. She could not brook the thought that the stone would be lost in the bowels of the earth. The sky would then turn into copper, the air fill with the foul smell of burning bodies. The leaves would fall and be covered by worms. The glorious sun would dim and turn into a lump of lead. The thought was too terrible. She knew Kandan was the cause and she was his wife. She, therefore, shared the sin. That was why she was searching for the stone. She must find it or die.

Nature knows neither pity nor remorse. The earth subsided and the dark woman vanished.

Tears rolled down Amal's cheeks. He sat motionless for a while. Then he continued,

Man never acknowledges defeat. Man is wonderful. The men of the village had been beating their breasts but now they were fired by a strong resolve. As ants restore their ruined nest, they descended into the deep abyss and, after three days, recovered the seat of stone.

It was a wonderful sight. The woman clasped the stone to her heart and it was spotless white.

MANOJE BASU

The Ghost

AT THE mouth of the Chandidaha, the boat became
unsteady. The current was strong and swift, and the
wind contrary.

The boatman had just lighted his hookah, but Haricharan
cried out, "You had better put it down and take to the
oar."

Haricharan picked up the hookah himself and, placing it
within his palms, started puffing at it with intense concentration. But to enjoy a smoke in peace was not his fate. Soon
there was a jingle of bangles from within the bamboo-and-
straw cabin. The jingle, of course, could be accidental—the
roof was low and one's hands might easily strike it. But the
bangles jingled again—once, twice.... Haricharan had to
leave his hookah and go in.

He found Prabha resting her head on a tin trunk, her hands
nervously clutching at its sides.

She pretended to smile and said, "Look how the boat is
tossing. And you go on smoking as if nothing is the matter."

"Are you afraid?" asked Haricharan.

"No. Why should I be frightened ? I am no cry-baby....
But what's this? Why have you come so close? There is only
five or six feet of space between us. What will the boatman
say?"

The gap was in fact not more than a couple of feet. But
Prabha was young—and they had been married hardly two
years.... One must not argue with her. Haricharan moved
closer and she snuggled up beside him, burying her head in
his lap.

After a while, she looked up and said: "Listen. If the boat suddenly overturns...."

"What a ghastly thought!" Haricharan said half angrily. "You must not say such things at this evening hour."

But Prabha would not listen.

"But suppose it happens. And don't forget that I can't swim. What will you do?"

"I shall swim across without looking back and reach home, alone but safe."

"Go on. You would never do that. But, honestly, why don't you tell me what you will do?"

"I shall carry you in my arms and swim ashore."

"But if you lose your grip? If I just slip off? The deep waters of the Chandidaha will swallow me. What will you do then?"

"Haven't you got anything else to talk about?"

But Prabha was insistent.

"Why don't you tell me? ... You won't? All right. You needn't if you don't want to." Her face darkened.

"I too shall drown myself. We shall be united at the bottom of the river."

"Nonsense!" Prabha shook her head. "How can a man drown if he knows how to swim?"

"Don't you believe me?"

"No."

"Do you think I can live without you?"

"Of course, I do. When I die you will not only be very much alive, but will be eagerly negotiating for a third wife. Talking of a man's love! Fiddlesticks!"

"All right. I don't love you. I can't buy you nice clothes or jewelry. I am a poor man. Of what use is my love?"

Haricharan turned his eyes away and gazed intently at the river scene.

Both were silent, but after a while it was Prabha who spoke.

"What are you looking at? The cows in the fields? The kingfishers? Or that fisherman's wife? Why don't you tell me?"

Haricharan remained silent.

Prabha sat up and, amidst a ripple of laughter, said:

"Don't be so angry.... All right, you do love me. You have heaps of love for me—one, two, ten thousand heaps of love! Are you happy now?"

She took Haricharan's face in both her hands and turned it toward her.

"I shan't let you turn your eyes away. Never. On the river, I feel so afraid. Look at me. Say something."

Haricharan had to say something.

"What shall I say?" he asked.

"Am I to tell you what you will say? All right. Say: 'I shall never smoke again, because smoking fouls the breath and Shrimati Prabhavati Devi does not like it....'"

"Easy for you to say," said Haricharan. "Haven't I told you of the severe trials during my early practice of smoking? Do you remember Nimu Das? Nimai of the fishermen's village?"

Prabha was a lover of tales. "Yes, go on," she replied with enthusiasm.

"I had struck up a friendship with Nimu. I was then at school. Every day I would funk my classes and go to Nimu's house. And wasn't he pleased to see me! He had a little plot of land on which he grew turmeric. Whenever I went, he would give me his spade and say: 'I will go and light the hookah for you. But do a bit of work for me. Dig the earth for the turmeric plants till I come back.' He wouldn't be back for an hour or more, and I went on digging the earth under the hot midday sun. Think of the price I had to pay for a smoke."

"Goodness me! So much trouble for a few puffs of smoke?"

"And that was not the end," Haricharan continued. "The story of my exploits reached my father and he beat me black and blue. I lost my faith in the world—I was then about twelve years old and I decided to become a sanyasi. In the early hours of a morning, I left home, with nothing but a box of matches, a packet of tobacco and my father's favourite hookah."

"Where did you go?" asked Prabha.

"I had no plans and went on walking. After every stretch of walking, I would sit under a tree and have a smoke. In the beginning it was great fun—smoking like a chimney in public. But the smoke was the only thing I consumed the whole day, and by evening the tobacco, too, was finished."

"Then?" Prabha asked in eager suspense.

"Then it struck me that there was no fun in being a sanyasi. The first thing I wanted was another smoke and shelter for the night. And then, if possible, some food. I saw a farmer carrying a bundle of dry palm leaves. 'Listen miah,' I called out, 'is there anything left in your hookah?' 'No,' came his flat reply. 'Which village is this?' I asked again. 'Kamaldanga,' said the farmer."

"Kamaldanga?" Prabha broke in. "Isn't that where Didi came from?"

"Didi?" asked Haricharan in surprise. "I didn't know that you had an elder sister."

"I mean Saraju. Don't you know? The one before me. Didn't you first marry in Kamaldanga?"

"No, that was Kalmidanga. Kamaldanga is far away, but Kalmidanga is quite near. We shall reach it soon."

"Really?" asked Prabha with great interest. "Will this boat go past Didi's village?"

"Yes, that's the only route.... Won't you take the Kalmidanga canal?" Haricharan asked the boatman.

But Prabha had no patience to wait for the boatman's reply. "I will get down at Kalmidanga," she burst in with excitement, "and have a look at the house of Didi's father.... Why are you laughing? No. I won't listen. Don't worry. I shan't be long. I will just go and be back in a minute."

"How can you do that?" Haricharan said.

"Why not? Do you think I have no relationship with Didi's parents? There will be nothing improper in my visiting them."

"Who's talking about propriety? But that house is far from the canal we shall pass through."

"How far? Two miles? Ten miles?——Go on. You are only trying to find an excuse to stop me."

Haricharan was going to say something in reply, but Prabha would not let him speak. She shook her head and said: "I know you will trot out one excuse or another, but I won't listen to you. I will go." Turning to the boatman she said: "Please tell me when we reach Kalmidanga. I will get down for a moment."

The old boatman agreed.

"Wasn't it at Kalmidanga that Didi died?" Prabha asked Haricharan.

"Yes. It seemed as if her fate dragged her here. After she came, she did not live for more than ten days. You have heard all that, haven't you?"

Prabha knew all about the tragedy. Haricharan, of course, had always wanted to avoid the topic, but Prabha had made him tell everything.

It happened four years ago. Haricharan was then employed as the manager of the Chaudhuri estate. An instalment of rent had just been collected and he was to take the money to the Chaudhuris who lived in Calcutta. The Rath festival was to be held in a few days and Haricharan had planned to do the shopping in Calcutta. He would buy some mango grafts and a set of fishing tackle. For Saraju, he wanted to buy a silk sari. The border must be chosen to match her delicate complexion. All arrangements had been made, but Saraju upset his plans.

It was evening and Haricharan was alone, going through his accounts. Saraju came into the room and made her proposal without any warning.

"I shall go to Kalmidanga with you," she announced.

Haricharan was engrossed with his figures. "Yes," he said absently.

"Then I will go and pack my things," said Saraju. She clinched the issue, and without waiting for a reply flew from the room.

Haricharan looked up and said: "Yes, what were you saying?" But Saraju had disappeared. When Haricharan saw her again, she had finished her packing. He tried to argue, but she said: "Didn't you say 'Yes'?"

There was no going back on it. Haricharan had to agree and make the necessary arrangements.

Rath was a great event in Kalmidanga and Saraju was to spend the festive days there. Haricharan would bring her back when returning from Calcutta.

A large boat was arranged. Saraju's father was informed so that he might meet Saraju at the Chapatala Ghat and take her home.

But all her enthusiasm died out when the boat reached Chapatala. She got off, and then turned back and told Haricharan: "I shan't go unless you come with me." But how could Haricharan break his journey? He was carrying a large amount of cash and must reach Calcutta in time to pay the revenue. But women are unreasonable. Saraju thought that Haricharan was annoyed with her. He tried to explain why he could not accompany her but she would not listen. She went on repeating: "I know you are angry. I can tell from your face. I insisted on coming. That's why you are angry."

Haricharan tried to laugh the matter away, but Saraju was not convinced. Saraju's father had come to receive her. He waited at the landing ghat and wondered if the farewell between husband and wife would ever end. Haricharan felt extremely embarrassed.

"What will your father think of us! Please go," he pleaded with his wife. But Saraju went on: "Tell me you are not angry. Touch me and say it. Promise that you will take me with you on your way back from Calcutta."

"Yes. I will take you," Haricharan promised as he held her hands.

But that promise was not kept....

THIS was all an old story. But all of it came back to Prabha's mind when she heard that their boat would pass through the village where Saraju's parents lived. She was looking through a large hole she had made in the flimsy roof of the boat. The north bank of the river glimmered faintly under the twilight sky. Prabha thought of her husband's former wife whom she had never seen. Haricharan, too, was full of pensive thoughts. The water splashed as the oars dipped in the river. A few fishing boats shot past like arrows. From somewhere in the dark, a little bird came out fluttering its anxious wings and flew over to the distant fields. The boatman shouted: "Pull the oar on the left. Away from the whirlpool on the right. *Gazi badar badar.*"

"Is it new moon tonight?" Prabha asked.

"No, that's tomorrow. Also the night of fasting. But why?"

"It was on a new-moon night that Didi died, wasn't it?"

"Are you still thinking of that?" said Haricharan as he looked fondly at Prabha. "Why can't you forget what has ended for ever?"

"Will you forget me completely if there's a similar end to me tonight?"

"What's come over you? Haven't you anything else to talk about? You must not say such things. There are fated hours and you never know when you make stray remarks."

Prabha smiled.

"Don't you believe me?" asked Haricharan. "Well, I too had no faith in all this talk about auspicious or inauspicious hours or in any conjunction of the stars. Little use had I for an almanac. But let me tell you what happened. When I left Saraju at Kalmidanga and reached Calcutta, news came from the estate that Bipin Shah and his men had breached the bund and let water into the fields. It was new moon and, on top of it, the day of the solar eclipse. The cashier of the estate told me: 'Don't stir out today. It is expressly forbidden in the scriptures.' But I paid no heed and I started for home. I thought that, on my way back, I would pick up Saraju from Kalmidanga. But the scriptures were right. When I reached Chapatala

Ghat, I found that there was no need for me to go to her father's house. She herself had come to meet me."

Prabha had not heard this before. "Did she come?" she asked. "But I heard that you never saw her again."

"Yes, she came," Haricharan replied. "I saw her—not at Chapatala but at the cremation ground, about a furlong to the west."

Haricharan fell silent again. He looked at the cluster of tall palms across the river where darkness was gathering fast. The sky was turning inky black, blotting out the stars one by one.

"Will you listen to me if I make a request?" Prabha asked.

"What is it?"

"Let us stop here for the night. We can start again with tomorrow's tide."

"Why?" asked Haricharan.

"If we reach Kalmidanga at night, you will never allow me to get down. I know that. It will be new moon tomorrow. We shall reach Chapatala by day and I shall run across to Didi's father and tell him: 'I have come back. Take me into your house.' I beg of you, don't say 'no'. My own father is dead, I'll go and win a new father tomorrow."

Prabha rested her head on Haricharan's feet and started crying like child.

But how could Haricharan take his new bride to the parents of his former wife? And that too without any notice. What would they say?

"Don't cry," he sought to console her. "Think it over calmly. Is it proper to go to a house where you are not known?"

"What is not proper?" Prabha asked, lifting her head.

"I will tell you. Sit up and listen. Why mourn for one whom God has taken away? It's best to forget."

"Yes, that's the only thing you can do," Prabha flared up and said. "You men talk of love, but it is all talk. Just hot wind. If there's a storm tonight and the boat sinks and I die, tomorrow you will find someone new to love. If she should ask about me, you will put her off with sweet words as you are trying to do now."

Haricharan laughed and said: "Have you closed your eyes in anger? Don't you see the boat has entered the canal. The water here is knee-deep. Even if the boat sinks we shall not be drowned. Look."

Prabha neither looked nor spoke. She was really angry.

The boat sped swiftly through the canal. Prabha sat gazing into the dark. It was a starless night and dark. She could see only dimly on either side. Here and there were small bamboo frames to support the creeping pumpkin plants. The water reached to the bottom of the bushes. A little beyond, the paddy-fields stretched out to the distant horizon. A few huts and hay-stacks lay slumbering on one side; from one of the huts came the sound of cymbals. The sky was overcast. There was no sign of anybody on either side of the canal. Prabha sat silent. Against the dark background of the shadow inside the boat, she looked like a painting drawn in gold.

Haricharan too was silent but after a while he could no longer bear this strange quiet. He took her hands in his and asked: "Listen, do you hear me?"

"Yes?"

From somewhere in the distance came a deep hissing sound; it had already started raining there.

"What are you looking at in the dark?" Haricharan asked Prabha. "Look at me. Are you still angry?"

"Why should I be angry?"

"Of course you are angry. This temper of yours is your only fault. Otherwise you are so charming."

"Really?" said Prabha, with a smile playing on her lips. She looked at Haricharan. "Is that so?" she asked again.

"Of course," said Haricharan, glowing all over with emotion. "I can lay bare my heart and show you how deeply I love you."

"Why don't you?" Prabha replied with a liquid laugh. "But tell me, how many times did you say this very thing to Didi?"

Haricharan felt suddenly crestfallen. Prabha was still possessed by Saraju's ghost! But what a question to ask! How could he remember if he had said this to Saraju? After all, a man says all kinds of things to his wife in the quiet hours of night. And at such hours, he might have told Saraju——but who remembers? Everybody says such things. In any case, this was not the time to make a confession. He shook his head and said: "Never. Not even once."

"Never? What a clear conscience!" Prabha remarked. "Are you sure you never told her that you would join her even in the bed of the river—as you were telling me a little while ago?"

Haricharan realised that Prabha was inwardly pleased, and his denials became more emphatic.

"Of course not," he said. "Do you think one can say such things to everybody. You are the only person to hear this from me. You know, although she was my wife, she never shared the love which is all for you——"

"Here we are at Kalmidanga," the boatman interrrupted.

The boat cleared its way through wild reeds which lay clustering over the shallow water and reached the landing ghat. The light on Haricharan's face died out. He was suddenly struck by the thought that Saraju had heard him say that he had never loved her and was moaning in deep pain. He could almost hear Saraju cry. The wind was rising to a storm. The bamboo stalks near the ghat groaned. There were other strange creaking sounds. It seemed as if someone was breaking down everything in a terrible confusion. It was all dark, but through the veils of darkness, he thought he could see Saraju standing on the cremation ground. He had not seen her for ages. Her face had faded in his memory, but tonight she stood clearly before his eyes. She looked as fair as ever. The large vermilion spot glowed on her forehead. She was dressed in a sari with a border of flaming red. It was she, there was no doubt about it. She was running toward him across the marshy land and through the thick bushes of wild plants. She had come quite near. But there was a bamboo bridge over the canal which she could not cross. She was calling out from the other side, waving to him, "Don't leave me here. Take me with you. Please take me."

Haricharan closed his eyes, put his hands on his ears, but he could not shut out the sound. He could still hear the unbroken wail of the storm—oo, oo, oo—a long and unceasing cry. The wail seemed to come from the other side of the bridge, where Saraju was crying and striking her face and breast. She had overheard what Haricharan had said about her. The ghost was crying for a man's love. A large tree fell with a crashing thud. The gale had grown in violence. And the ghost, it seemed, was now going to cross the bridge and come to the man for whose love it was wailing. Haricharan wanted to cry out to the boatman: "Take the oar. Quick. We must get away."

But he could not utter a single word.

SANJAY BHATTACHARYA

On My Birthday

Light-footed birds of light
Fly back to the golden nest of the sun.
Night descends.

Night comes and asks me,
"What have you given to the earth?"
What have I given? Nothing.
Rather have I taken what you have scattered aside
The lady of the night, champaks and jasmines.

The same question flames
Out of the blue light of the stars:
"What have you given to the sky?"

Nothing have I to give.
I have forgotten the language of the earth.
Forgotten what flowers
One needs to weave the garland.

PRAMATHANATH BISI

The Padma

O Padma
On your far horizon denuded of the line of trees
The tired sun melts drop by drop
And finally the last drop sinks.

The unruffled water is spread far and wide
Like the spread wings of a brown dusky bat.
In the west is a blaze of colours.
The forest is dim and tense.
The liquid shadows deepen every moment.
Your dancing movement is quick and light
Like an apron of lightning,
O Padma.

There is green moss on the river.
The grass is burned with the sun.
The parched fields give out a vegetable smell
With the touch of fresh dew.
The wind is heavy with its own scent.
All this is yours,
O Padma.

The twilight bells ring
In the smoke laden village path.
One hears the steady beat of oars of solitary boats.
Suddenly comes the swish
Of the eager wings of homeward swans.
I saw in the gathering darkness
The glow of the evening star
Above the tall mast sunk in the heaps of sand.
All this is yours,
O Padma.

B U D D H A D E V A   B O S E

A Parting

After the first thousand nights we had to part.
Rain fell on the river, the water rose in flood;
Between the bamboos, like a hidden hope,
One or two fireflies fitfully gleamed.
The sky was closed in cloud, but not quite,
For the wound throbbed sometimes, as lightning flicked
And a long, low moaning perished in the pain
Of trying to utter the inexpressible.
Urgent, uncertain, ruthless, full of violence,
The water foamed and spread and disappeared
Into the final silence of the Fates
When I left my love in the hand of God.

Still gazed a lamp in the little room;
Close to the trembling heart a limp white hand
Rested upon a tenuous quilt[1]
Stitched with torn-out fragments of the past.
Remembrance flung itself upon my feet,
And the door grew dim with persuasion:
It meant but quicker work for the knife within my flesh.
Winds began to howl in impatience,
Hungering for islands of exile
Or some barely possible shore of distant time:
Meanwhile the whole deep dark exhaled
A curious odour of childhood and sleep—
Fantastic tokens of security—
That night I left my love in the hand of God.

[1]The word in the original is *kantha*, which is a kind of light cotton quilt made out of old discarded clothes by housewives and grandmothers in Bengal. Humble in origin, they are sometimes things of beauty and handed from one generation to the next.

The future, already on the way,
Filled out the sails in shapes of pregnancy;
Ferment of whatever is to come
Tore the ropes and rocked the bony deck
With such turmoil of indecision
That weeds writhed like snakes, fish took fright and scuttled,
Bumping against the helpless keel.
But, desire, tough in captaincy,
Held out against the treacherous tide
Where I saw my corpse afloat, and heard among the waves
Semblance of one undying name
Interminably reminding me
That I had left my love in the hand of God.

Images of a dark and desperate need
Rose like a tower and fell away
As the blind, implacable boat pursued
The drunken kiss of waves and distance.
Sleep came at last. An infinite sleep
Broken, twisted, agonized
By the stupid necessity of keeping awake.
And yet, I know, that small house still is there
Calmly of the earth, among sprouting leaves.
At the doorway, in dim light
Dead ancestors crouch and gently confer
In cautious tones about the doubts and fears
That the smooth, impassive clock conceals.
It's right for them: but I, who still have time,
Have not a thought, or skill, or choice
But to leave you, love, in the hand of God.

A M I Y A   C H A K R A V A R T Y

The Traveller

A mountain village in Iran:
Our car halts under linden trees,
The heart of a poppy field
Opens with a red silky sky, and a warm mild scent.
Stepping out on the road, between Qasvin and Kerman
A dusty traveller, I open the thermos bottle, take
       the mountain scene
And busily look at the map: Where am I?

Unknown clusters of homes, strange life, alien tongue,
Kindliness in eyes, blue and domed mosque,
Life blossoms a desert rose.

Where am I?
Spreading heart's harvest, and blue wind on the hills,
And children's looks from under pulled down caps,
Some voice reached my receding ears, across the
       heavy car's horn
—Hardly did I hear—
"Amid willow's murmur and the voice of waterfalls
       in houses.
With the green rug of grass spread under trees,
And gardens with tea served in noon day's light,
Rest awhile,
For you are H E R E:
In this World, your home."

Throwing the haze of quick dust, the car races,
Smothering an age of beauty's miracle,
Under far unrest.
Back to nearness, in my distant home,
At travel's end
The gift of a lost day I seek and the home that is
HERE.

Two Days

It has rained at the end of *Magh*.
The first morning of *Phalgun* is scattered over the fields.
The mist of the night is dripping in the sun
Like pale timid love.
The forlorn village girl
Seeks in the earth for marks of Lakshmi's gracious steps.
Placid and self-possessed farmers
Drive their ploughs strongly through the soil.
A magic dream clings to the far-flung fields.
The farmers sweat drips into the soft earth.
I asked the peasant girl, "Let us go home."
She scattered the seeds from her apron and said:
"I have no time.
The bare fields are full of hunger for seedlings.
How can I return home
And leave their desire unfulfilled?
I have much to do now.
You better come some other day."

It is the tale of another day.
Heavy autumn dew pours upon the bare fields.
Meadows and roads are hid in an apron of mist.
Peasants have carried away the harvest.
My eyes are tired with crowds and festivities.
The heart hungers for the quiet comfort of the night.
At last the tumult ends
And quiet descends on the village.
I again asked the peasant girl:

"Let us go to the fields."
She replied, "I have no time.
Look, we have brought in the harvest.
The farmer's wife sings the song of new crops.
I have never seen so rich and full an autumn.
How can I now go to the bare field
That lies empty like a mother whose child is dead?
There is much work on my hands.
You better come some other day."

Sailor

The sailor has a sense of defeat as he gets up with a start
And finds that instead of taking his post at the helm
He had dozed off hoping that his ship at mid sea
Would take care of itself.
He pulls himself together, resumes his position of watch and toil.

Sun—the din and hurry of a port nearby
And the row of palms hail him.
His ship moves on.

To the priestess with a shock of golden hair
The evening sun seems like the egg of the bird of paradise,
To the farmer a plaything amid his acres of ripening wheat.
Human heads huddled together in dark
Have a glimpse of Sunray's slant
Piercing like a lance into their hovel;
They look, rapt, at the golden beam and the motes in it
Rapidly throbbing and flying—flying and throbbing; why?
                                        to what end?

O Sailor, you press on, keep pace with the Sun;
You have been caught awhile in the mirrors of Babylon,
                        Nineveh, Egypt, China and Ur;
Loosened yourself and headed for other shores,
The impulse from Vaishali, Byzantium and Alexandria
Has been to you like thin, straight candles glowing on
                                        remembered beaches.
They are good, but whet the quest;
You want deeper knowledge, completer experience.

As long as honeybees with wings sparkling like spray fly in
the sun
And the heron with a surer touch than the jet plane
Brings home the virgin vastness of the blue
Man will not rest content;
Purged of follies, sin and tragic mistakes
His sailor-soul will fare forward
To move into a better discovery of life on this planet,
A greater joy—a deeper communion.

SAJANI KANTA DAS

The Two Poles

My mind has its two poles
The North and the South:
But they are not both ice-cold.
My north pole is cold and ice bound.
Faint sunless light flashes on it momentarily
Like the pale smile on dead lips.
If life is there or sparkling water
They are frozen beneath the massed ice.
The pole is cold,
The tempests are full of chill.
Even our breath freezes and rises like smoke.
No birds fly there.
No trees, no nests.
Only the penguins stumble across with frozen wings.
The whale and the seal hide timidly in the cold dark
And disturb the ice cold water.
The hairy bear totters like a drunken man.

The north pole of my mind
Knows no end of the aurora borealis.
Deathless and frozen cold
Shadeless light:
The flow of time itself is frozen there.

In the south pole of my mind
Boils blood red lava
The hairs turn grey and drop
The leaves are scattered.

For a moment the wind is heavy with the scent of flowers
But then comes a hideous smell.
Good and bad, the beautiful and the ugly
Are carried forward by the stream of time.

There is the roar of the ocean in my southern pole.
The blue water glitters in the bright sunlight.
Millions of sea animals play among the violent waves.
Touched by the sun they sink into the depths of the sea.
The foam is scattered on the crest of waves,
They seek to touch the sky,
They strike vainly at the wind like a serpent.

All the rivers of the earth meet in my south pole.
It is muddy and full of whirlpools
Dead bodies drift across
Wood and straw and leaves float by—
The message of life and death comes from the rich earth,
The message of light and darkness.
My companions of the way are stormy winds
A bird with broken wings.
The kites fly.
The kingfisher shoots to the sky.
There are whispers, laughter and shouts.
Sometimes they sing in unison
Sometimes they sing alone.

The south is my youth:
It is full of meaningless babble.
Warm enjoyment and warmer laughter and tears
Day and night walk across like painted prostitutes:
Desire lifts up its head like a hooded serpent
The terror of the forest charges the waters of the pole.
The beautiful and the ugly mingle
And make me unique.

The north pole remains in the north
The south in the south.
They do not know one another,
Their only unity is in my heart.
They revolt against each other in futile and unknowing rage
Their conflict and clash within my heart,
Their discord rises like poisonous mist,
Turns the ugly into the beautiful
And beauty into ugliness.

I live with this mingling of the north and the south,
Secretly my heart bows before the unknown God,
And tinged by the scarlet mark on oppressed women's brow,
Giving everything to the poor
And robbing those who are already cheated.

In the south I belong to all,
In the north I belong to myself alone.
In the north is my grave in the shadow of the wayside tree
The flowers are scattered on it by spring's restless wind.
Strangers come and weep for me—
Death itself died there long ago.

I love the south but the north loves me.
The north prepares my grave and waits for me.
I cling to the south and seek to raise
Barriers against the north.
I do not know if dark death
Will unite my north and south and make me one.
Perhaps it is for this I wait.

S U D H I N D R A   N A T H   D A T T A

The End

I spent the rain-dimmed day in absent-minded reverie.
I opened wide the doors of my solitary heart
To make the passage of memory simple and easy.
With unseeing eyes I saw in the brooding sky
The picture of a day like today.
In the ceaseless lament of the rain
I heard the fond address of a familiar voice.
In the vain storm blasts on the closed windows
My heart, torn with parting, protested in powerless rage
To the silent, stern and passionless God.

Evening descended bereft of rain.
Like the last momentary splendour of a dying light
The day's dying torch burnt bright with a last effort.
Then darkness spread its death-like mantle
On my heart and on the outside world.

I felt there was no hope.
I felt there was no language to express my caged despair.
I felt that death was closing all around
And pressing me in an iron vice.
I felt that like a rat that moves along narrow holes
I have all these days stolen particles of grain
From the stores of many misers.
Today the game is ended:
At last the deadly trap has closed on me.
When now the door would lift,
My poor beggary would be crushed under the lifted broom.

BISHNU DEY

A Sonnet

Golden the cowdust hour, yet in my hollow heavens
Burns the arid dream of an afternoon. O my heart lost in blue!
Ecstasy grows pale over the flaming fields and forges
In desire, in love. Yet the awkward heart is cold.
I set sail on love's magic waters, yet scarred and torn,
It burns, for Lethe is but dead and dry.
O village cowherd, O coolie-on-the-railways, let life
Flow, let loose the floods, make me current and common.
Let this discord of body and mind, the world and self,
On the mound of the Hydra's head sing into a green tree
Strong and straight in the trunk, intimately earthy,
   Yet various in its airy foliage.
Let the Timons abdicate from their doubts and debts,
And look! Hegel's vainglory lying low on the ground
In factories, in ploughlands, in the floor paintings of Matisse
   In the street-rallies of Mallarmé's pupils.

AJIT DUTTA

The Question

If some day the wind becomes listless
And the sky radiant with the colour of my heart
In autumn or in music flooded spring,
And tries to wipe out dark dreams of night
With the breath of new birth:
Will then this mock theatre of the world
With its learning and warfare,
Its politics and trade and commerce—
Will all these things drop out and disappear
In the depths of the heart
In that moment of magic meeting?

If my tired feet after long wandering
On the turfed earth damp with dew
Suddenly find back the track
On the borders of some vast field
Or on the banks of a forgotten river:
The strange joyous music of a home of love,
Small villages or green woods
Nestling among grey hills,
The ancient sky and the ancient stars,
Suddenly released from silent meditation
Will they bend down on my heart
And inscribe on its pages a new poem?

I have sought that moment with tired steps.
In towns and markets
In fairs and fields and green
In forests
And in the crowds that cluster on the roads of the city.
I have sought it in the lone magic casements of fairy tales
In days showered with gold
In nights scattered with diamonds
On the crest of crowded millions
Or all by myself on the solitary shore,
In islands and deserts and places of pilgrimage.
From the top of minars that tower high
I have sought with wide open eyes.
I have sought in all quarters of the globe
And I have felt it by and yet far away.

Many days have passed.
The morning light has now turned
Into the evening shadows.
This final questioning of my heart
Is still waiting for a final answer
In the sky, in the wind and on the moon.
Sometimes in the homes of men
In the songs of birds
And the gentle murmur of love,
Perhaps in life or beyond life
That moment waits for me expectantly.

NARAYAN GANGOPADHYAYA

The Fly Trap

T H E telegram said that a third daughter had been born
to Bimalendu. Mother and child were both doing well
and he need not have any anxiety on their account.

The telegram had come from his esteemable father-in-law.
Obviously, he hoped that the son-in-law would be delighted
at the news. In fact, however, Bimalendu looked wild when he
read the telegram. His face had been transformed and looked
strangely foolish. The two dull eyes reminded one of a bullock
that had been made to work hard in turning the oil mill for
hours on end. Perhaps it was the thought of the expenses he
would have to incur in marrying off another daughter that was
troubling him.

For full five minutes Bimalendu puffed like an engine
working up steam. At last he let off a sounding breath and said,
"So it is all over."

I asked him what he meant.

"My youth. All my dreams of love."

Bimalendu paced up and down and spoke in a pathetic tone,
like that of a man who had been robbed clean by a pick-
pocket. "All romance is now gone from my life. From a man
with a future I have become a man with a past," he said.

I told him that it was better so: "You may become a respectable citizen if you can get through your youthful
escapades so soon."

Either Bimalendu did not hear me or, if he did, paid no
attention. He declaimed dramatically, "I now realise that
love can never become tangible. The moment the beloved
becomes a wife, all our life's dreams begin to wane. Plato's

love of beauty, his dreams of bodyless union...."

I interrupted him and said, "That is how the impotent seek to console themselves."

Bimalendu became wild. His melodramatic pose became even more marked.

He said, "Wife, children, a safe job, where you do every-thing according to a fixed routine . . . all these are like the life of a tubercular patient. It is far better to have uncertainty, the open sky, the horizon stretching to the far distance, sweet flowers of mahua and a lovely Santal maiden...."

It was difficult for me to restrain my laughter. I did not know if Bimalendu had ever stepped outside Calcutta. Perhaps he might have visited health resorts like Madhupur or Deoghar or cities of pilgrimage like Puri or Banaras. It was of course natural that he should dream of boundless horizons and sweet mahua flowers !

I interrupted him again and said, "You are wrong, Bimalendu. The flower of the mahua is not sweet but rather bitter. It does not however matter. In fact the natural sequel to love is possession—the only apt comparison is with the Venus flytrap, haven't you seen the flower? You will imbibe a little wisdom if you read Schopenhauer. But it is not man's love alone that is possessive. Nature's love is also all consuming."

"Are you talking of the African jungles?" asked Bimalendu.

I replied, "No, I am thinking of things nearer home. The open fields of Bengal with the unbounded horizons, her stret-ches of paddy lands and the clusters of wild tulsi, her sky washed with golden autumn...."

Bimalendu interrupted me and said, "I do not understand you."

I told him a story of my childhood:

Y o u know that most of my childhood was spent in a small village in Bengal. I was then young. It was the age when love appears in a man's life like the first experience of intoxication. Those were days when the world before us seemed like pages from the Arabian Nights. If I woke up on a moonlit night, I would not go to sleep again, but sit near the window and gaze into the distance. If the rain came and washed my head and face, I still did not move away but watched the rain coming down. Even the tiny flowers which bloomed in the grass seemed familiar friends. The pungent smell of the wild akanda seemed to speak to one's blood.

It was at this stage of my life that I spent years in a village in Bengal. It was a little-known railway station on an unfrequented branch line. Even the slowest of passenger trains did not stop there for more than a minute. The handful of travellers who got in or out from villages all around did not disturb the stillness of the station for more than an hour or so throughout the twenty-four hours of the day and night.

There was of course the far-flung and solitary world. There was a murmur of the palms on the hillocks of red mud. In the distance bullock carts moved in a cloud of dust. Here and there were fields of maize or, in the lowlands, paddy. Wild ducks now and then flitted across the sky. A thin straggling stream flitted weakly through the scene. In the midday the road-metal bed of the railway line shone brightly. The line wound by fields of maize and was lost in the distance. It was a branch line which started from the junction station, but I did not know where it went. I could imagine it travelling as far as Delhi, Bombay, Kashmir, and the Kara Koram Hills, and perhaps beyond, till it reached the land of the penguins at the North or the South Pole !

My uncle was a station master. He had not married. A switchman looked after his household affairs. Once he returned to his quarters after finishing his work, he opened a book of Vivekananda or some other religious writer. He was a serious-minded man and never opened his mouth unless he had to.

How was I to spend my days? I felt the call of the earth in my blood. I discovered myself anew in the fields of maize, on the railway line, and on the banks of the tiny river.

Finches and cockatoos danced on the telegraph wires. Many coloured butterflies flitted over the elephant grass. The golden sun seemed to stir my blood like wine. I moved about as if in a dream. I had made myself a fishing line and used to go and sit by the river. The silvery water trickled through mud and pebbles. Tiny fish flitted about in the thin stream. With infinite patience I used to sit in the hope that I would hook a fish.

Somehow the river had harmonised wonderfully with the sky and the wind. Here and there were patches of elephant grass or clusters of the wild tulsi. I did not then know I was in love with these wild tulsi plants. They had red stalks and tiny impudent leaves. The winds stirred them easily and they waved. It seemed that a murmur flowed through stalks and leaves. Their flowers shed a wild and pungent smell. I would become restless, for the smell suggested to me a new taste of the far-flung world.

I had made myself a little nook inside the clusters of wild tulsi. That was my favourite fishing haunt. Angling was only a pretext. I used to cast the line and gaze either at the railway line or into the distant sky. At other times, I used to tear the blossoms from the wild tulsi and rub them till the smell became a part of my being. Perhaps some Freudian complex was working in my subconscious, but the real fact is that I was in love with the wild tulsi.

S U D D E N L Y human love appeared against this wild background.

There was nothing to get excited about. The place was lonely and few people ever came there. I was therefore surprised when one day a little girl suddenly appeared on the scene.

Perhaps she was a tribal girl—a Turi. She was eleven or twelve and her sari reached hardly up to her knees. She had a little basket in her hands. She had come to collect sand from the river. She was dirty and her face was bespattered with mud. She burst out laughing when she found me gazing at her. I remember I found her smile very sweet. Perhaps there were other reasons for it. The sky was then full of autumnal gold. The water of the tiny river was sparkling. The cluster of wild tulsi was bending before the wind and in my blood there was the aroma of wild flowers. I kept looking at her in speechless wonder.

The girl asked me, "What fish have you got?"

I replied, "Nothing."

The girl retorted, "You will not get any fish. You may catch some frogs."

This was certainly not the type of language one would expect from a heroine when she first met the hero. I was going to reply equally tartly, but before I could say anything she gave me a mocking smile and disappeared.

The fishing rod lay idle in my hands. I sat there for long. I was slightly drunk with the autumnal sun, with the aroma of the wild tulsi flowers. For long I thought about the girl without any definite purpose. No, it was not a case of being carried away by first love. In fact, whenever I remembered how she had made faces at me, I felt that I would like to slap her hard, if only I could get hold of her.

I started going to the spot day after day. Often I thought that this slip of a girl had made a fool of me. If I met her again, I would teach her a lesson. That opportunity never came. She was the first heroine in my life but she disappeared after the fleeting vision and never returned. Perhaps it was better so. If I had seen her again, I would have certainly thrashed her. What would then have followed, I do not know. It was perhaps because I did not avenge myself for my discomfiture that I could never forget her. She remained as my first beloved in my subconscious mind. She remained a part of my world of the wild tulsi.

Thus I lost the first heroine in my life. Then I lost that

small station, the fields of maize, the lines of palm on the
hillocks, the silver stream, and the forests of wild tulsi. I left
all of them behind and came to the city. It was a new life in
a new environment. I was immersed in my school and college,
in arts and politics and literature.

The strong smell of the wild tulsi no longer clung to my
hands, but it lingered in my blood. Often in the night I saw
in my dreams the thin red stalks waving in the wind. I could
hear in my reveries the gentle murmur of the tiny leaves.
There was often a surge of emotion as the idle moments of
romantic thought were charged with a strong and pungent
smell.

So far it was all good. I was in love with the wild tulsi, but
I did not realise that the tulsi forest had also fallen in love
with me. I have already said that it is the nature of love to
possess. In the case of human love, there is no need to argue
the point. It is a self-evident truth. I did not however know
that the fields and meadows of rural Bengal were also capable
of the same savage love.

I T happened about five years ago. I had just taken my M.A.
degree and was looking for a job. I looked at all the advertise-
ments in the newspapers. Whenever there was a vacancy,
whether it was for a schoolteacher or a university professor,
I sent in my application. Needless to say that I was doing good
to nobody but the postal department. Disappointed, I was
wondering whether I would abandon the world and devote
myself to the study of the *Gita* and other religious scriptures
when I received a letter from a friend. It was an invitation
for a shoot. He lived in one of the wild and marshy areas of
North Bengal. It was a hunters' paradise for the place was
brimful with wild duck. I was a fairly good shot as I had been
a member of a secret political society and practised at targets
hidden in mango groves. I would now get a chance of testing
my marksmanship in the open. Besides, I was longing for an

outing. I accepted my friend's invitation with alacrity.

I really liked the surroundings of his home. I had almost forgotten that the sky was so large and uninhibited. There were open fields and marshes all around. One came across numberless wild ducks and cranes, snipes of all sizes and even a few floricans. It was a paradise for the small-game hunter.

My friend Sudhir was a well-to-do farmer and possessed a couple of guns. We went out to shoot in the intervals of the generous hospitality one always finds in the villages. We created havoc among the lotus reeds and in the quiet and untroubled world of the wild ducks. We went out early in the morning and when in the evening we returned with strings of blood-stained ducks, we felt as if we were conquerors. We were possessed by a strange and ferocious joy, by the lure of the hunt. When these wounded birds writhed in pain and their blood stained the dark water of the marsh, we congratulated one another with triumphal cries that were almost inhuman. When, on the other hand, the ducks defeated our wiles and flew away out of our range, our thoughts were dark with sullen anger. In a word, the hidden killer in us was out.

One day Sudhir said, "Are you prepared for a long trek?"

I asked, "Why?"

"There is no fun in killing these ducks. I have news of bigger game."

"Big game? What is it? A tiger or is it a bear?"

"No, no. I am not thinking of tigers and bears. There are some swans."

"Swans?"

"Yes, a large breed called Italian swans. A flock flew over here last night. I heard their call for the first time this year. I had sent out to find where they are resting. I have now learned that the flock is feeding on a *jheel* five miles away. This is a vast flock. There are about a thousand birds."

"How do you know they have not already flown away?"

"No, no," said Sudhir. "This Kamala *jheel* is an excellent place. There is no human habitation for over three miles all around. The birds are never disturbed. Besides, these swans are somewhat fearless. If they find a place they like, they do not easily move away. Shall we go tomorrow?"

"Let us go," I said.

Sudhir remarked, "But you will have to walk over five miles. We must go on foot. We could go on a bullock cart but we would have to go by a roundabout way. It would be over ten miles and take the whole day."

I remarked, "We had better walk."

Sudhir said, "You are not accustomed to trekking. You will perhaps find it too much of a strain."

The killer in me was awake. I said with enthusiasm, "It will be no hardship at all. Besides, I must behave like a Roman when I am in Rome !"

We started next morning before it was light. We had hats on our heads and flasks strapped to our shoulders. A servant was carrying the tiffin basket and the guns. We were five men in the party.

The path led through binna shrubs which reached up to our waists. We walked over narrow tracks between the paddy fields. Before we had walked a mile, the sun rose in a blaze of scarlet. I have been to Puri in summer but have never seen its famous sunrise. I have only heard descriptions. I have sought twice or thrice to see the sunrise on Tiger Hills. I have shivered in the terrible cold but the cloud and fog mocked me every time. I have heard that sunrise on the sea or in the hills is an unparalleled sight, but have you ever seen the sun rise on the vast plains of Bengal? If you have not, you have missed a rich experience.

The sun rose across the fields. All the seven colours of the rainbow were painted vividly on the sky. A large blot of blood suffused the water of the *jheel* and the distant forests. I shall never forget the sunrise I saw that morning. I felt the smell of the wild tulsi in the bright sunrise.

I was the last in the line. Some rubble got into my shoes and I had to stop and take it out. After I had done so, I lighted a cigarette. I found that my companions had moved on. This did not however bother me. The path lay across the fields. I could never think that I could lose my way. The binna shrubs were no doubt becoming taller but I could clearly see the hats and the guns a little ahead.

I walked along slowly. The autumnal sun was spreading over the world like a fine mantle of silk. My path led me to a small canal. There was a bamboo bridge across but, as I was about to step on it, I was struck with wonder by what I saw.

There rose before me a Venus built in black marble. She was a Santal girl in the first flush of her youth. She stood behind a curtain of binna shrubs and was carefully washing herself on the bank of the lonely canal. She was unadorned and fearless like the world which stretched all around. In the golden sunlight, her bare body shone with a wonderful glow.

It is certainly against good taste to stare at a naked girl, but the wild open fields and the magic sunrise had removed me so far from my familiar world that my training, culture, and habits had dropped like a discarded robe. There was no desire in my admiration and I certainly did not look at her with lust. My whole consciousness was full of a sense of the wonder and beauty of life. It seemed to me that the water of the canal, the light of the sun, the smell of the trees had all united and together built up a vision of beauty: an image that had no relation with any earthly thing. It seemed that in a moment the image would disappear and merge in the water, in the light, and in the sky.

I do not remember how long I stood spellbound. At last she picked up the clothes which were lying at her feet. She dressed herself carefully and walked slowly along the narrow track through the paddy fields. She walked on and, in a little while, disappeared beyond the clusters of wild tulsi, the tulsi with which I had been in love throughout my adolescence.

In a moment, every drop of blood in my body was charged with my childhood memories. The echo of a song from far away swept through my consciousness. I felt on my hands again the strong acid smell which I had smelled when I was a child. I forgot all about my companions and the way I had to go. All my thoughts were turned upside down. It seemed to me that my lost first love had returned today in the full bloom of her youth and was waiting for me among the shrubs of the wild tulsi.

Was it an idle day-dream or was it cheap romanticism? Perhaps that may be the explanation, but I have already told you that the sunrise this morning had strangely moved me· The flavour of the wild tulsi was stirring in my subconscious. Perhaps a sudden incursion of elements from my subconscious had prevaded my conscious mind and upset all the everyday standards. Without a moment's thought, I followed the girl into the shrubs of wild tulsi.

It seemed that there was after many years a perfect symphony of autumnal sunlight and soft mellow winds. After many years, the soft red stalks again put out their arms to embrace me. The rough leaves of the wild tulsi touched my face as if in loving caress. I went forward through the dense shrubbery without knowing where I went. Was it in search of the lost heroine of my early youth? Perhaps it was not even that. The touch of the stalks and leaves of the tulsi and the powerful smell which emanated from the plants that I trampled combined with the murmur of the wind through the shrubs and became the only reality for me.

After I had wandered for about an hour, I felt tired and sat down on the ground. No, I did not sit on the ground, for the shrub was so thick that there was no ground to sit on. I sat on the stalks and leaves of the wild tulsi and the plants surrounded me on all sides. It was like a wall which towered over my head and hid me from the rest of creation. There was nothing to see on any side, except the deep blue sky above and torn fragments of clouds that floated about like the petals of a white lotus.

I sat there by myself for hours. I was feeling the closeness of the wild tulsi with my whole being. My senses were dazed with their touch and smell and my mind slept. Unknown to myself, I smoked perhaps half a dozen cigarettes when suddenly I came to myself. It seemed that reality again touched my immersed consciousness. I remembered I had come out for a shoot with my friend, Sudhir. Perhaps they were worried about me. Perhaps they were thinking I had lost my way.

I looked at my watch and found it was almost eleven. I had no idea it was so late. I filled my pockets with leaves of wild tulsi and got up to return. I had however reckoned without my host. The wild tulsi had also found me after many years. I was willing to leave her now, but not she. She clung to me in close embrace. I wanted to get out of the forest, but found I was helpless. I then realised how foolish I had been. You were saying a little while ago that the Platonic is the only safe form of love. I agree. For men as well as for nature.

It seemed to me that the tulsi forest had no end. It seemed the shrubs continued to the horizon and beyond. A strange magic had transformed mountains and oceans, villages and towns, in fact the whole world into a forest of wild tulsi. My past life, my culture and training, my friends and relations had all become an illusion. I suddenly feared that I could never get out of this forest of tulsi—never. My blood was frozen with an unknown fear and the hairs stood on end on my head. My love for the wild tulsi had now changed. It was a blood-thirsty animal which with a thousand arms held me in close embrace. The plants were red with the thirst for blood. The leaves were rough and serrated in hunger for my flesh.

The autumnal sun rode high in the sky and hurt me with its intensity. My eyes became dim. I sought to push my way through the forest of tulsi but in vain. The forest had no end and I would never find my way out. I lifted up my head and tried to look over the tops of the tulsi plants, but as far as the eye could see, there was nothing all around but tulsi plants on the uneven ground.

With all my strength, I sought to go forward but felt weak and helpless as I struggled through the forest. Several times

I stumbled as I tried to go fast. I lost one of my shoes and I knew it when my purse was flung from my pocket. I was not however in a condition to look for either of them. My one thought was somehow to get out of this murderous forest of wild tulsi. I remembered distant Calcutta, its many buildings and houses, the trams and buses which move on the road: the normal life of day-to-day. Here I was dying by inches inside the forest of wild tulsi and no one would ever discover me.

Several times I tried to cry out but who was there to respond to my cry? There was no one to hear my wails in the empty fields that stretched from horizon to horizon. There was no way out, no way out indeed. I felt I would suffocate or perhaps die of snake bite. I would not be surprised if a tiger suddenly came out.

With a last effort, I tried to move forward but my feet caught in the roots of a dense cluster of the wild tulsi. I fell down on the ground and felt as if the tulsi plants clutched at me like a brood of vipers crawling over my body. Before I lost consciousness, I suddenly realised that I was about to die and that my body would turn to dust in an unknown grave. When I was dead, the manure I had supplied would make the tulsi plants stronger and more cruel. They would obliterate me and completely swallow me.

FORTUNATELY for me, Sudhir noticed my hat lying just on the outskirts of this forest of wild tulsi. He came with a party and rescued me from the web which my first love had woven for my destruction.

That is why you had better stay in Calcutta. Life here is simple and simple is the love of man. You may one day die but you will live in your children. The world of man will not obliterate all trace of you like the cruel love of nature.

S A N T O S H   K U M A R   G H O S H

Devaluation

M ANMATHA tapped on the door several times but it
did not open. Then he called, "Savitri!"

From within the room came a cautious voice: "Who is that?"

"It's me."

The door opened. "Why are you so late?" said Savitri. "I have been half dead with fright all this time. I sat stiff on the bed and could hardly move."

Manmatha pulled off his vest and said: "How could I come earlier when I had two private tutions in hand. Could you fan me for a little while?"

With his chest bare and his dhoti pulled up to the knee, Manmatha enjoyed the breeze from the hand-fan for five minutes. But Savitri did not tell him anything then. She told him much later, while coming to bed, about the events of the day.

About mid-afternoon, a taxicab had honked right at the mouth of the alley. A minute later a pair of creaking shoes had stopped before their door. And then a tap at the door. Alone in new lodgings and without any acquaintances there, Savitri had become stiff with fright. The door had been already held with a pin-bolt but she had further fastened the cross-bolt. Fortunately, at that very moment the door of the next room had opened and a whispering voice had said: "Not there, but here. Have you become completely blind?"

The man of the creaking shoes had said: "Is that so? Sorry, I made a mistake. Are you ready?"

"Quite ready."

"Then steady—go!"

The creaking shoes had faded away, followed by a tap-tap sound, probably from high-heeled shoes. A moment later had come the sound of the taxi moving away from the alley-mouth.

Manmatha listened to the end and then said, "You are feeling uneasy over everything because it's a new place. When you come to know the people a little you won't be so afraid."

Savitri had not liked their new home or the alley itself from the very first. Of course, she had pressed Manmatha to set up a separate home: but did it have to be like this? In her father's place at Behala, a Calcutta suburb, there was at least a touch of Mother Earth and they had a roof with an umbrella of cocoanut palms overhead. But in this narrow alley of Ahiritola (a crowded quarter of Calcutta) all they had was pitch and stone.

In this tenement house, one hardly felt the passage of time. The day was like a girl with a stunted body. After a sleepless night of dank heat, the gaslight in the alley closed its tired eyes and with it man, too. But only for a few minutes. And then the main street awakens to noise. The first tramcar clangs its way with a load of early bathers to the Ganga. The water drops into the storage tank from the household tap with a low gurgling sound.

And everything runs to set time here. Family bosses are going to market: so it must be half-past seven. They return home with bags full of shrimps and leafy vegetables; eight o'clock. Jostling one another at the bathing-yard with mugs in hand and a few hurried splashes on the body; half-past eight. A wolfed meal: nine o'clock. A cone of betel, a cheap cigarette —one from the day's ration of six—lighted from the roadside faggot-rope: it is half-past nine and now a frantic sprint. . . .

And then the alley falls adrowsing with not a sound disturbing its length except the infrequent cawing of a crow or the tired footfall of a street vendor seeking, not so much customers as rest in the shade.

Only once in the afternoon does the alley return to life when the taxicab honks at the alley mouth. The three-tap signal sounds on the next door and the sound of high heels fades in the wake of creaking shoes.

It took six days to get acquainted.

As Savitri was putting a vermilion mark on her forehead in front of the mirror placed on the window-sill, she saw the reflection and turned round. "Please come in," she said. "Don't you live in the next room?"

Two hesitant feet on the door-sill. Savitri took in the high heels with a swift glance.

"I would rather not enter with shoes. I'm going out now. I noticed the last two days that you are newcomers. I didn't have the time to make your acquaintance earlier. I find the door always shut. Today I found it open and have come."

"Do please come in," Savitri said again. "You need not take off your shoes, my husband always comes in with shoes on."

Sitting on the bed, the woman said: "How fine! You have put everything nicely in order. Well, it's a household of two persons."

"Not two," said Savitri with a shy smile, "three."

"O ho, so it is. I missed seeing the baby altogether. How quietly she sleeps! Who has she taken after?—her father?"

"How could I say?" Then, becoming bolder, Savitri asked: "How many are you, Didi?"[1]

The woman almost collapsed with laughter. "What was that you said? Didi? I am Mallika. You may call me Mallika-di, for I think I must be older than you."

"Mallika-di," Savitri asked, "how many are you—three or four?"

"Only one, dear," replied Mallika. "One and nonpareil. Since we are not even a pair, how could there be a third?"

"Oh dear, haven't you married? Why didn't you?"

"Was it of my sweet will? It just didn't happen," Mallika replied in a disinterested manner. "But I can't stay long, my dear. I have to go out. Time for the beckoning flute."

---

[1]Didi: form of address for elder sister.

"Beckoning flute?" said Savitri, a little puzzled. "Oh, you are referring to the taxi. You must be moving about in taxis frequently?"

"Ah yes—I do. Don't you?"

"Me?" Savitri's eyes clouded over with a film. "Me? What an idea, Mallika-di! I came from one poor family to another— I have been in a taxi only twice in my life, once on the occasion of my marriage and then this year—on the way to hospital the day Minoo was born." She made a sign to indicate her daughter.

After this Savitri could not restrain her curiosity. She asked: "Who comes everyday to fetch you? That man with creaking shoes, coat, trousers . . ."

"O dear, you have noticed him!" Mallika said with the ghost of a smile. "He is—well, he is a son of my maternal aunt. He takes me every day for a little airing because I have got a bad heart."

Next day, after finishing her meal, Savitri herself went to Mallika's room. Mallika was in bed, reading a book. "Come in, my dear. Finished your day's work?"

Far from moving in, Savitri's legs were rooted to the doorstep. It was a small room, but she had never seen such beautiful appointments. On a brightly polished bedstead was spread an impeccably white bed. The pillowcases were embroidered. A dressing mirror, a teapoy, a gramophone. A large variety of glass and china playthings in the almirah.

"These?" Savitri asked.

"Dolls," said Mallika. "I play with them, don't you know? Have I become too old to play with dolls?" she asked playfully.

Savitri seated herself very carefully on a corner of the bed. "My clothes are soiled and I am afraid . . ." Then pointing at the book in Mallika's hands, she asked: "What is it you're reading?"

Mallika said, folding the book, "A novel. It's the story I saw yesterday at the cinema. Very moving. To tell you the truth, dear, at two places tears came into my eyes."

"Oh, you had been to a cinema yesterday?"

"Had to go, but not of my free will. I had a headache through-out the afternoon but he wouldn't listen."

"Who didn't, Didi?"

"No, no, not Didi? Call me Mallika-di. It was my cousin—my paternal uncle's son."

"Your uncle's son, Mallika-di? Younger than you?"

Computing his age on her fingers, Mallika said, "Much younger. By two years, maybe. Why, haven't you seen him? That's him who comes with a car every afternoon. Well, he is in the cinema business. A director."

Savitri did not tell Manmatha immediately, but long afterward, at night, while cooling his platter of steaming rice with a hand-fan.

"What kind of a house have you brought me to without making inquiries?"

Manmatha stopped eating and looked at his wife with inquiring eyes. Savitri whispered: "Didn't I tell you the other day? Our neighbour—she's a bad woman. How I can put up here? You are out for the whole day and you don't see what happens."

After a pause she added, "The other day she had said it was her maternal aunty's son. Today he has become her paternal uncle's. Although I am uneducated, I can guess the sort of relationship when cousins change sides overnight."

Manmatha resumed eating. "Do'nt worry about them," he said. "It's all right if you keep right. I know you well enough to be sure that nothing evil can come near you."

The knowledge that her husband had implicit confidence in her incorruptibility filled Savitri's heart with pride.

IN THE morning, as Manmatha was about to start for his office, Savitri said: "You must find another place right today."

"All right," he replied.

It was eight at night before Manmatha returned. Opening

the door to him, Savitri asked: "Have you found it?"

"What?"

"Another place."

Manmatha doffed his shirt, hung it on a hook but did not reply.

Setting his meal before him, Savitri said, "If you don't look for a new house tomorrow, I tell you I shall create a scene."

Manmatha retorted in annoyance: "Is it so easy to get hold of a house?"

"Bah! Won't you look for one for that reason?"

Sucking in a mouthful of lentil pottage out of a bowl, Manmatha said: "Of course I will. But will such haste be of any use?"

Savitri threw the ladle with force on the floor and bitterly complained: "You should have made inquiries before bringing me into a brothel."

Manmatha stopped eating. He said: "Have I brought you to a brothel?"

Savitri's eyes were still flaming. "What else is she but a prostitute?" she said in a choked voice. "She paints herself all day long like a harlot. There is no mistaking what kind of a woman she is. If you don't make arrangements, I will make mine. I shall go to my father's house right tomorrow."

Pouring water on his platter to signify his resolve not to finish his meal, Manmatha said angrily, "All right, go. As if I did not know how comfortable you would be there. Your father is dead and your mother is completely under the thumb of your brother and his wife. Didn't you have to slave all day and do all the housework there? From changing the diaper of your brother's son to doing the family washing? Didn't you have to cook the meals and pocket insults daily? They don't even have two sleeping rooms. When I used to visit there on Saturdays, they used to give us the attic above the stairs and your old mother had to lie out in the cold and have a racking cough all night. Didn't you then implore me in tears to set up house for ourselves? Didn't you say you would be happy to live with me even under a tree? And now you talk in another vein. Have you picked up all this from your visits to the theatre?"

Savitri was taking out a mat to sleep upon the floor. Manmatha asked: "Won't you eat?"

Savitri lay flat on her stomach and dug her head into a pillow. In a voice broken with suppressed tears, she said, "Today you've gone to the length of taunting me about my father's place. I won't touch anything, not even water."

"Won't touch any food, is it?"

"No."

"Very good." Manmatha took a pillow and went out to sleep on the open terrace outside.

Next morning, as he woke, he felt heavy in the body. Consulting the mirror inside the room, he found his eyes red. Savitri had in the meantime bathed. She placed a cup of tea before him and was about to go when Manmatha called her.

With her wet unbraided hair cascading over her shoulders, her forehead looked pale and mellow like the early morning sky. Her eyes were soft and tired with nightlong weeping. Manmatha stared at her but could not bring himself to speak. Savitri stared down at the ground. After a long time Manmatha called, "Savitri!"

Savitri raised her eyes. Her eyelids fluttered and became a little wet, her lips trembled. Manmatha rose, faced Savitri and placed one hand on her shoulder. Savitri wanted to move away, to push away his hand, but could not. On the contrary she moved nearer and downed her weeping face on his breast.

Next minute she raised her shining face. "What, your body is hot!"

Manmatha just smiled.

Savitri said, "And you slept out last night in a fit of anger! You aren't going to office today."

"It's nothing," Manmatha said. "I must go to office. You were mad after a new house, so I haven't told you yet. Our office staff is being reduced; everyone lives in fear. Absence may cause trouble."

Savitri stepped back as if she had received an electric shock. In an apprehensive voice she asked, "Will you, too, lose your job?"

"That's quite possible. Our business depends on imports and exports and imports are not coming regularly now. Exports to Pakistan have ceased."

After a short silence, Manmatha resumed: "Do bear up for a little while. Let there be something final about my job. Let's not invite new worries over a change of diggings in the meantime." In a lower, more confidential, key he continued: "We may be poor but we are pure of heart. Let's not lower ourselves by doubting each other. You know me and I know the stuff that you are made of. Everything will come right so long as we value each other."

Manmatha had gone for the morning shopping when Mallika stood at the door. Smilingly she asked: "So husband and wife had a tiff last night !"

Savitri said, rather ashamed, "Why, no."

"O ho—now we are denying it."

"But how did you know?"

"Ain't I a clairvoyant? Well, I looked into the magic glass in my room. No, dear, not that, but I eavesdropped. I listened through the hole in your door."

Savitri was still unconvinced. So Mallika finally said, "Last night I saw your husband sleeping out. That's how. I went to the last show at the theatre and came back late at night. Don't you see my eyes are a little heavy? That's because I didn't sleep well." After a little pause she said, "Last night you too didn't have any sleep. If a thief came, he would have been in trouble," Mallika commented with a laugh.

But Savitri did not laugh. And to cover her embarrassment Mallika had to laugh harder.

Y o u can't cut your neighbours however much you may want

to. You have to return one civil smile for another. And specially when, a few days later, Mallika brought a gift of a big bowl of fowl curry, she couldn't well refuse it. She had to return the compliment with another bowl of carp's head cooked in cabbage, bought from a good hotel. Manmatha was furious over the matter of expense, but only for a few minutes. Mallika was duly appreciative of the excellent cooking.

A few days later Mallika was very busy at noon rearranging her room. The walls were cleared of cobwebs and dirt, the floor was cleaned with buckets and buckets of water. The bed was removed to a corner. The mirror was carefully polished. The vases were filled with fresh flowers and over the carpet was placed a snow-white bedspread.

Herself she had soaped profusely at the bathing-yard. Savitri met her on the verandah, after having watched her at her toils.

"Why all this to-do, Mallika-di?"

Mallika smiled mysteriously. "Don't you know? They will be coming to approve me as a bride. As I have no one to take care of me, I am doing it for myself."

"You are joking," said Savitri.

"Why, don't I qualify for a bride? Have I grown too old to marry, my dear? Look, how firm and white my skin is." Mallika extended her hands forward.

Embarrassed, Savitri protested, "Certainly not. But please tell me seriously, Mallika-di, who is coming today?"

"A few friends. I have asked them. They will be coming presently."

Now Mallika sat before the mirror and set about her elaborate toilet. Her shampooed hair she puffed out with expert fingers. With a little rouge, powder and cream she mixed a charming make-up for her face; her brows she painted with a pencil. And Savitri was fascinated when she showed her even pearl-white teeth in a dazzling smile.

A little later Savitri said, "Your friends are due any moment. I should make a move now, Mallika-di."

"Stay on for a while," pleaded Mallika.

There were still some things to be done in the room. Mallika began re-arranging some bric-à-brac; and Savitri, sitting on a stool, looked with wonder while the baby sucked at her breast.

Right into the room walked the creaking shoes, not one pair but several. It was impossible to escape through the room's one door. Savitri was greatly embarrassed as she arranged her clothes. She felt herself exposed to foreign glances.

But somehow she managed to do it. And, then, with the baby in her arms, she tried to hurry out through the door when she discovered Sasanka, Mallika's persistent cousin, right on the door-sill.

Sasanka had very heavily perfumed himself. It nauseated Savitri. He stepped aside a little and Savitri, rushing out through the gap, had an uneasy feeling of having been touched by unclean, bejewelled fingers.

Even in the sanctuary of her own room, Savitri could not forget the way Sasanka had looked at her. How sensual, how greedy it was—like the craving of a starved cat to lick a bowl of milk or a fish-bone. Her whole body shivered with disgust.

It was a Saturday and Manmatha returned home earlier than usual. No sooner had he stepped into the room than he almost shouted, "What is on in that room?"

"Can't you talk lower?" said Savitri. "Music. Mallika-di is singing. Many visitors have come."

Manmatha's face was distorted with loathing. He closed the door and the window with a bang. "For shame—for shame," he hissed. "It's too much, I say."

Listening for a while, Savitri said, "Don't I hear ankle-bells, too?"

Manmatha was then considering whether to close the two ventilators also. "Don't listen," he ordered.

The music went on intermittently, one song following another. At each pause Savitri thought the entertainment would end. But no, after each song there would be a burst of hand-clapping and applause, and the harmonium would break forth into a new tune.

"How scandalous!" declared Manmatha. "So this is your Mallika-di's profession! Now it's quite clear. For shame! How ignoble can a human being become for a bellyful of food!"

His face lit up: "But we have this pride, Savitri, that even if we die of starvation, we won't debase the inner man. I will speak to the landlord tomorrow. Some steps must be taken."

Savitri had thought that Mallika wouldn't be able to face her the next day. But surprisingly enough, it was Mallika who accosted her as they met at the bathing-yard.

She was so shameless as to ask: "How did you like my songs last night?"

Savitri did not reply.

Mallika went on: "What a strain it was last night! They wouldn't let me stop. As soon as I finished one song, they asked for another."

Savitri asked obliquely: "Did your guests approve you as a bride?"

Mallika broke into loud laughter: "My God, you still hold on to that joke? They didn't come to inspect me. We had a rehearsal of an opera which we are going to stage soon. The show will be on the coming fullmoon night. Do you know, a theatre hall has also been engaged?"

Savitri silently went on with her washing. Mallika suddenly came so near as almost to touch her and whispered in Savitri's ear: "Please be a little careful, dear. Yesterday Sasanka saw you clearly at close quarters. I must admit he has been completely bowled over. They have a small part of a mother in the film they are now shooting. You were feeding your baby at that time—they want a scene just like that."

Probably Mallika would have said more in her mood of confidence, but just at that moment Savitri stamped out of the yard. As she went she looked back and said, "Isn't it better to die, Mallika-di?"

O n Sunday Manmatha felt too lazy to carry out his threat

and visit the landlord. He was due to go on Monday on his way back from office, but he came directly home at three in the afternoon and went straight to bed.

Savitri, who was enjoying her siesta, sat up hurriedly. She asked: "How did you manage to come home so early? Since you have come, you must take me to a cinema."

Manmatha gave her a hard stare. "Yes, it needs only that to complete our bliss. You have chosen a wonderful time for such festivities."

Savitri approached him timidly and put her hand on his brow. Her cool damp hands felt some heat, but she could not be sure. So she placed her cheek on his brow and said with relief, "No, you don't have any fever."

Manmatha edged away. In a cold, sad voice he said: "The reply is not engraved on my brow, Savitri, but in the breast pocket of my shirt. Go and look."

As she saw the envelope bearing the printed name of the Company, her face blanched. Without opening the letter she asked: "What is this—retrenched?"

Manmatha replied by covering his eyes with his hands.

M A L L I K A peeped in and said, "O dear, you've already put the baby on rice? How old is she—has she cut any teeth?"

Savitri hurriedly said: "O yes, six on each side. She has had such a bad stomach that I am thinking of putting her off milk today."

Mallika suppressed a smile. "Calcutta's milk is only one-fourth water. I think it would be better than rice which is full of stone."

Savitri noted the manner in which Mallika suppressed a smile, felt irritated and cursed her under her breath: "Bawdy bitch."

In the evening, Manmatha was drafting an application for a job and was smiling to himself. Savitri seated herself beside him and asked in a low voice: "I see you are smiling. Have you received any hope?"

"No," replied Manmatha. "I am thinking of how I made a fool of the Superintendent of Alfred Jackson & Company today."

Seeing that Savitri was curious, Manmatha went on: "Well, when the fellow looked at my unshaven face and bare feet he almost refused to speak to me. Then he said, 'There's no vacancy for an office boy, try elsewhere.' Instantly a plan flashed in my brain. I said, 'I am not after an office boy's job, sir, but a clerical job. I have seven years' experience at Simpson & Joseph's.' He looked me up and down—the damned fellow's eyes were like a pair of brushes—and gulped, 'You!' I said, 'I come from a respectable family, sir, and I am an undergraduate....My father's brother is dead, so I am in mourning.'

"At once the fellow's face registered a different expression. He said, 'Come with an application after the mourning period is over and let me see what I can do for you with the junior director.'" Manmatha broke into loud laughter.

"See him with an application, then," Savitri said.

"Well, there's the rub. I could take the application right tomorrow. I could, of course, get my beard shaved for two annas and say that the funeral rites are over. The problem is how to cover my feet."

Without a word Savitri took off her wedding ring and placed it in Manmatha's hand. Before Manmatha could speak, she said: "You must buy yourself a pair of shoes tomorrow."

SAVITRI tried to avoid Mallika and not to be intimate with her but Mallika would not let her alone. Whenever she found Manmatha was out, she would come into Savitri's room. She would embarrass Savitri with a series of searching questions.

"What, you haven't put even a bodice on, Savitri?"

Confused, Savitri tried to gather her sari over her bare body and excuse herself: "You see, it's so hot today."

"Hot? You make me laugh, dear. It has been raining throughout the last four days, there's a cold wind, we have to cover ourselves at night with sheets and yet you go on feeling hot? You amaze me, my dear. This must be the heat of youth."

Savitri felt her anger rise. She would have liked to strangle Mallika and tear her to pieces. But nothing could be done; no one could be told anything about this suffering. This privation that was twin brother to starvation had to be kept concealed like a secret ulcer. But how long could she hide it?

"I'll be going out today," Mallika confided. "I came to ask you to keep an eye on my room."

Savitri did not ask where she would be going, but Mallika volunteered the information.

"Going to the races, dear. Sasanka and his friends are very insistent. I don't know if I can stand the strain of a whole day's outing."

She took a long breath and continued: "However, Sasanka is really a clever chap. He'd make you a winner all right. Five hundred chips for five. Don't you know of that magic trick?—you hold a handful of dirt and it becomes gold? It's like that."

"Five hundred for five, Mallika-di?"

"Well, in a manner of speaking. But if it happens to be the right type of horse, it's not impossible. And if you chance to click on the daily double, then it's even bigger—you become rich overnight."

Savitri's eyes were like stars. Mallika asked, "Why do you look amazed?"

She replied in a parched voice, "No reason at all."

But no sooner had Mallika gone out than Savitri delved into the pot which stored the rice and brought out a small tin and, out of the tin a small bundle which, when untied, released a number of copper coins—a total of twenty-one pieces. She had kept it apart as a votive offering to the deity in the event of Manmatha landing a job.

Mallika had not yet finished dressing when Savitri stood

before her. Mallika was then powdering the more visible parts of her body. Looking round, she asked, "What is it, my dear?"

For a long time Savitri found she could not speak. Then, setting aside her diffidence, she said in a low voice: "Can one bet with small amounts, Mallika-di?"

Mallika's face was suffused with laughter. "How small my dear?" she asked.

"Well, let's say five and a quarter annas?"[1]

"Why five and a quarter—five annas will do. I know many bookies; will you bet?"

With hesitant, trembling fingers Savitri placed 20 pice[2] coins in Mallika's hand.

"Which horse?" Mallika asked.

Said Savitri, "I don't understand anything about it. Please do what you think best, Mallika-di."

Those five annas, however, came back with interest. "Your luck is good," said Mallika. "We betted wildly and lost everything but the horse we put your money on won the event. But the payment was not good, it was a favourite, don't you know. Five annas fetched only eight."

"That's good enough for me," said Savitri as she tied her prize to the hem of her sari.

Manmatha was astonished to find himself served with savouries along with his usually bare tea. "Where did you get the money for this?"

Savitri smiled mysteriously.

Disappointed again and again in his effort to land a job, Manmatha had become sour and irritable. Savitri's silence enraged him and in a huff, he taunted her, "So this is your earning?"

Even the insinuation could not wipe off her smile— "If I say yes, what then?" she asked.

---

[1]An *anna* is worth about 1.25 cents in American currency and slightly above a penny in English currency.

[2]A *pice* is a quarter of an *anna*.

"I shouldn't be surprised," Manmatha retorted rudely, "specially when there is a blooming model of virtue next door."

Savitri was broken-hearted at Manmatha's remarks. She told him everything.

Manmatha's face darkened. Gravely he said, "In one sense this is an evil earning. It's a great shame. Don't I tell you, Savitri, that we should keep off these things? I would rather starve than live on such earnings."

LATE that autumn Savitri went to stay with her parents. She did so unwillingly, and at Manmatha's insistence. She had pleaded that she did not mind hardships. Besides, who would be there to care for him?

Manmatha replied, "Don't worry about me. In your present condition you wouldn't be able to stand the strain of hard work. Besides you don't get even two square meals here. It might lead to some mishap. And then, it will be only for a short while. The child is due after five-and-a-half months, isn't it?"

But right on the twenty-fifth day she came back, pale and as thin as a scarecrow. Her Adam's apple had become prominent and her abdomen seemed to press against her spine.

Mallika said, "I was hoping you would return with a baby in your arms. But what is it I see, my dear?"

"It's been a blessing in disguise. A new baby would have been an enemy," said Savitri. "What would we have fed him on?"

"What happened darling?"

"Nothing special, I was not feeling good when I went. Had slight fever every day. Then one day I swooned at the bathing yard, and . . ."

"You might have stayed on till you recouped your health a little."

Savitri was silent.

FOR some time past Manmatha had been constantly out, professedly on business. Before she went, Savitri had been told that Manmatha was working on commission for a friend who had a printing press. They had scraped together everything they had to raise the price of a monthly tramcar ticket.

One day, seeing Manmatha lying quietly after his midday meal, Savitri asked, "Well, sir, aren't you going to work today?"

Manmatha yawned, "All bunkum. Only running about here and there, a mere wearing out of the body."

"Couldn't you place orders for your friend's press?"

"Well, I did." Manmatha pointed to a heap of letter-heads stocked under the bedstead. "Didn't you see those? Chuckerbarty & Dutt—Order Suppliers?"

"Which company is that?"

"I am the company. I added the 'Dutt' because a single name sounds too bare. Sell off these for waste paper tomorrow."

Another proposition for a job fell through after it had advanced a good deal. It was as a trade representative for a business firm. The salary was one hundred rupees per month, daily allowance and 2 per cent commission on sales. Manmatha had even paid a little money to secure favourable consideration. He went for an interview on the appointed date. On his return Savitri anxiously asked, "Successful?"

"No," said Manmatha. "Swindlers—the bally lot of them—wanted a security deposit of five hundred rupees. Well, would I have made off with your goods? Couldn't you trust me to this small extent?"

Manmatha grew excited as if it were Savitri who had asked for the security deposit or had not trusted him.

"Did they take in another man?"

"Yes, that's what I am coming to. The lucky candidate is known to me—Prabhas Ganguly, who married the other day for a cash dowry of six thousand rupees. So he promptly coughed out the five hundred."

Savitri hung her head in self-abasement, although there was

no earthly reason for it. Her father had given her in marriage
without any dowry or even a trousseau. Did Manmatha regret
his rash nobility now, after one child had arrived and another
had been lost on the way?

Y o u can hide the cake in your mouth, but how can you
hide the tell-tale swollen cheeks? And Mallika had so surprised
her that there was no chance of concealment.

"So early at your meal?" asked Mallika.

Savitri had just sat down to a meagre plate of rice and
boiled leaves. On other days she had pretended that she had
finished her meal or that her husband had been too busy to
do the morning shopping or that she had no appetite. But
today she was caught redhanded.

Mallika went back to her room and returned with a small
bowl of fish curry. "Will you just sample it, my dear, I am not
certain I added the salt to it."

The pretence was very transparent and had it been former
days, Savtri might have refused to accept it. But it was different today. Savitri's eyes became moist. What mistakes men
make! How they repel others for little or no reason! Why did
Savitri have a settled dislike for the girl in the next room?
Was it because she had tried to conceal her real character from
her? Suddenly Savitri realised that she on her part had concealed many things from Mallika. Mallika had wanted to keep
secret her burden of shame and Savitri her burden of want.
After a long time Savitri felt for the first time that both of
them were equally poised on the brink of disaster.

A flood of salt tears welled out of her eyes.

That day Savitri embarked upon an act of great daring.

T h e sun was not very warm but Savitri felt her eyes smarting
and her ears hot. Her sari hampered her, for she was unused to
walking. The straps of her borrowed sandals dug into her skin.

As she had never come out alone, she was afraid she might miss the way. But Mallika had carefully instructed her and it did not prove difficult.

The clock indicated it was about a quarter of an hour before the movie show would begin. She plumped down upon a couch and wiped her perspiring face on a scented handkerchief loaned by Mallika.

Today she had concealed nothing from Mallika. Manmatha was out of a job. They did not know how to make both ends meet in spite of frequent fasts. She set aside all pride and sense of prestige and begged Mallika to provide her with some work. "I do not care for myself," she had sobbed. "But I can't sit idle and see my baby dying of starvation."

"What work can you do?"

What work—she had pondered. She had not read much nor did she know sewing. So she could not be a teacher or a tailor. She was not even smart enough to be a telephone girl. She conquered her reluctance with great courage and proposed: "Well could I have the job you had mentioned the other day? That small movie job—a mother's part. Would you please speak to Sasanka Babu[1] about it?"

Mallika sat silent for a long time. She bit a piece of thread and pondered. At last she said: "It may come off if I tell him; there is an easier way, however. But would you agree to it, my dear?"

"Agree?" her feeble laughter had become heavy with tears. "Beggars can't be choosers. I am afraid of nothing now, Mallika-di. Tell me."

Mallika told her. Savitri, who had shown much eagerness, was silent for a time. Mallika emphasised: "I am not advising you to do anything wrong. All you have to do is to sit beside him. A ticket is already booked in my name. I am convinced that it will be ten times more effective than if I tell him. It is the best policy to move for yourself, my dear."

[1] Bengali equivalent for Mr.

There was a hypnotic quality about Mallika's firm voice and steady eyes. Savitri was stirred to her depths. As if from the bottom of a well, a flat voice came through: "Very well, I agree, Mallika-di. Give me the ticket."

And so she had come to the movie. Manmatha was out and she did not even wait for his permission.

With the switching off of the lights Sasanka came in and sat beside her. Savitri's body shivered and she huddled on her seat. It was Sasanka who exclaimed in amazement: "You!"

"Mallika-di is indisposed and could not come. The ticket was going a-begging, so she . . ."

In the darkened hall, shadowy figures were already moving on the screen and talking. In the auditorium, there was now a burst of loud laughter and now pin-drop silence. Savitri had neither eyes nor ears for these. Her throat was parched, her body was numb and her eyes felt dry and burning. She was afraid that a hairy arm would paw at her under cover of darkness or the hand of covetous desire grasp her by the waist. Every time Sasanka stirred, she fidgeted and moved aside in fear. Times without number, she placed her hand on the arm of the next chair and withdrew it. Once she heard a rustle and thought Sasanka's left hand was straying in search of something. With a supreme effort, Savitri stiffened her body and made her mind ready to face what she thought was coming. And then there was a spurt of light. Looking sideways, Savitri saw him light a cigarette. He had been fishing for a box of matches in his left pocket.

Savitri took out her handkerchief and wiped the sweat from her brow.

As the lights went up at the interval, Sasanka went out and returned with two ice-creams. Handing one to Savitri, he asked, "Are you liking the show?"

What she mumbled with a nod in reply she herself did not hear.

"Can you follow the story? Shall I buy you a programme?"

"No," said Savitri.

"What illness is Mallika suffering from?"

Haltingly Savitri improvised, "Nothing very much. Well—a little headache."

The lights went off again. Again that ash-grey pall of thin darkness, the ceaseless progress of talking shadows and again that breath-choking fear, that clammy uneasiness. Savitri did not, nor did she want to, understand anything. She alternately placed her hands on the chair-arm and withdrew it, moved toward and away from her neighbour. Time and again she heard the pounding of her own heart afraid of the contact of rude hands.

As the lights went up for the last time, the spectators started streaming out. Savitri mechanically followed Sasanka but it took more than five minutes to come out.

"Will you have some refreshments?" Sasanka asked.

Savitri wanted to say no, but could not get out a word, for she had lost her power of speech. They sat in a small, curtained-off cubicle. "What will you have?" said Sasanka.

In a diffident, dry voice Savitri managed to say, "A glass of water, please."

"You can't have only water," Sasanka said and ordered some eatables.

So long as they were in the theatre Savitri had her eyes upon Sasanka's hands. Now her eyes were rivetted upon his feet under the table. Those creaking shoes. Savitri shivered and withdrew her own feet under her chair. Yet she could imagine the stealthy advance of a pair of feet pressing down upon the sore spot where the thongs of her sandals had cut into the delicate skin.

Sasanka asked: "You don't look like a regular movie-goer."

At last Savitri clicked into sense. She suddenly remembered the business for which she had taken so much trouble.

"No," she said. "You see them quite often, don't you?"

"Me? I have to. You must be knowing that I am in the movie business?"

Time was running out. Sasanka was slowly sipping his tea.

Presently the waiter would come with the bill. Now was the time to say whatever had to be said.

Still she could not say it straight. She started with petty questions about studio work—how they shot scenes and synchronised sounds etc. etc. Then she wanted to know about the pictures he was shooting.

"Only one," said Sasanka, "and that, too, is making little progress. It is a bad market now. Everybody is afraid because of heavy losses."

The hope that Sasanka might himself offer her the job was fast receding. The waiter had gone to fetch change for the five-rupee note Sasanka had paid against the bill. The last moment had arrived.

In desperate urgency Savitri said: "Mallika-di had told me you have a role vacant—yes, vacant—in your picture and were looking for a suitable artiste."

Sasanka's brows contracted above a pair of gay eyes. "Mallika told you? When?"

"Some time back." Savitri was no longer afraid now that she had taken the plunge. With bent head she went on: "We are in great want, Sasanka Babu. So I thought I might—might . . ."

Sasanka tapped a cigarette hard on his match-box a number of times. He said, "You are too late, madam. When I told Mallika, we were in search of an artiste who could act a mother's part in a natural manner. We have somehow managed that. The picture has been finished and is awaiting release."

Savitri's face was drained of all colour. Yet with the desperation of a last gamble she asked, "Haven't you any vacancy for any part in your new picture?"

"Yes. But not a mother's role. We are looking for a heroine.

"But". . . Sasanka examined her from head to foot . . ."Excuse me, madam, I don't think you will do for that role."

Savitri could see a clear reflection of herself in Sasanka's eyes. Her face flushed red with sudden shame and then was drained white like parchment. A brow widened by receding hair, a pair of sunken eyes within black rings, high cheekbones and a prominent Adam's apple, thin hands with protruding veins, two raised nipples on flat shapeless breasts—without saying a word Sasanka had rubbed it home that a heroine does not look like that.

"I am very sorry I can't do anything at present," said Sasanka. "But I shall keep you in mind and shall let you know if there is any opening in the next picture."

S A S A N K A was good enough to offer to see her home but Savitri did not accept the offer. As she hurried home the clock in the store gave her a fright. Evening had come; baby must have awakened and started crying. Manmatha must have returned and discovered her absence. Surely he would be black with rage. There would be no escape today. Savitri saw in her imagination Manmatha pacing the room with clenched fists and compressed lips. What would he do on seeing her? Shut the door on her face? Throw her out on the street? Or start a row, a scandal for her offence of stepping out without his permission?

When she went out impulsively she had not even remotely thought of these possibilities. How insensible women become when ruin inexorably approaches them!

The door was ajar. Manmatha, lying flat on his back, had the baby on his chest and was trying to lull it to sleep. Savitri changed her clothes with her face against the wall.

"The show over?"

Savitri did not know what to say in reply.

Manmatha said with a smile: "Well, I know. I found on returning that your Mallika-di was plying baby with crackers and toffee to keep her quiet. Heard about it from her."

Manmatha's face was very serene, his voice was absolutely without heat. Savitri jabbed at the floor with her toe-nails. Rather than such a heartless joke, she would have preferred a straight rebuke or even violent fingers at her throat.

Manmatha said reassuringly: "Good, good. It's very good that you are trying to make your own way instead of sitting in a corner like a decrepit old woman." Then, lowering his voice, he asked: "How did you get on? Did Sasanka offer anything?"

"What should he offer?"

"Take, for instance, a job. They have so many contacts, they may find a job for you. But didn't you ask for it?"

"No."

On a sudden Manmatha sat straight up on the bed. He asked in a hard voice: "Then why did you go? How can a man understand what you want unless you explain it to him?"

"I am not in the habit of spinning out words."

Manmatha seemed to lose his temper. "—Not in the habit? Priggish puss! You are not a puling baby. Don't you even know what is good for you?"

Keeping her voice calm, Savitri asked, "What?"

Without replying to the question, Manmatha enquired: "Sasanka did not offer to escort you home, did he?"

"Yes, he did, but I didn't accept it."

"Y-e-s—h-e—d-i-d—but I d-i-d—n-o-t accept it," Manmatha mimicked her words with heavy sarcasm. "Why not?"

"Wouldn't it have injured your dignity if I did?"

"Does your dignity feed you?" Manmatha shouted. "How would it have injured you if Sasanka had escorted you home in a car?"

Manmatha was staring at her steadily. The pupils of his eyes were like bits of live coal. Savitri was startled as she tried to meet those fiery eyes. Only now she realised that Manmatha had not been ridiculing her. He had really wished Savitri to come with Sasanka in the same car. Perhaps she would then have received the gift of a job.

Manmatha continued: "They are gay people and like a little merriment. They come in useful if they are pleased. You have spoiled everything by your prudery."

With an impulsive gesture Savitri put her hand on his

mouth and sobbed: "Please stop, will you?"

Then without waiting, she reeled unsteadily into the next room and threw herself face down on Mallika's bed. Mallika quickly seated herself beside her: "What has happened Savitri? Why are you so moved?"

The answer was inaudible. Savitri's voice had broken in her desperate effort to suppress her sobs. Gently stroking her back, Mallika said, "Tell me all that has happened, my dear. Has Manmatha Babu taken you to task for going to the movie without his permission?"

Savitri indicated by repeated shakes of her head that it was not so.

"Then?" Bringing her lips to Savitri's ears, she asked, "Is it that Sasanka was too fresh at the theatre?"

Not even that, Savitri again indicated by a shake of her head.

"What is it, then?"

There was no reply. Savitri was indulging in an orgy of weeping. How could she explain where it hurt? All these days she had believed that her body had value for Sasanka, if for no one else, while her purity had value for Manmatha. She could never tell anyone—far less Mallika—how both the illusions had been shattered in a single day.

S U B O D H   G H O S H

The Waiting Room

W H A T train was it that panted its way to the station through the rain and darkness so late at night? Most likely it had brought passengers who had crossed the Ganges on the ferry. One could still hear the siren of the ship. She had ferried one batch of passengers and was now starting for the bank across with another batch.

It seemed that the engine was gasping for breath as it stood by the platform in Rajpur Junction. The waiter in the First Class Waiting Room got busy dusting the tables and chairs and wiping clean the mirror. The sweeper also cleaned up the room with his broom.

The train from the river bank was only a shuttle and the number of passengers few. Most of them were Santal coolies, but there were always one or two who travelled First. Perhaps the proprietor of a sugar mill from Katihar or the Manager of a tea garden in Darjeeling.

The two passengers who hurriedly entered the First Class Waiting Room on this particular night had however nothing to do with either sugar mills or tea gardens. The first to arrive was a young Bengali woman in a fine cashmere coat. Her small emerald eardrops and the stylish hair-do proved her fine taste. A porter lumbered behind her with luggage heaped on his head while she sailed in through the drizzling rain.

The passenger who followed close on her heels had also the inevitable suitcase and bedding piled on the porter's head. He was spectacled and dressed in Indian clothes with a shawl thrown over his shoulders.

A gentleman and a lady travelling by the same train had

sought shelter in the same waiting room. This was their only relation, if relation it can at all be called. Perhaps he would wait for a couple of hours and she a little more. Then, when their trains came, each would go his or her own way.

It was strange that in this case the two passengers started as soon as their eyes met. For a moment, they stood still like painted figures. It seemed that both were taken aback and felt shy, awkward and perhaps a little annoyed. It almost seemed that they were afraid to meet. Their plight seemed to be like that of two escaped prisoners who had been captured and put into the same dock. The raindrops glistened on Madhuri Roy's coat. Satadal Dutt looked dazed through his wet glasses which he forgot to wipe.

This waiting room of Rajpur Junction was not the dock in a court. There was no one to ask questions nor extort confessions. Yet it seemed that they found this close proximity unbearable. Perhaps they would feel easier if they could part. Satadal moved up to the door and called for a porter.

Satadal could move his luggage and go out. He did not know where, but he felt that almost anywhere else would be better. Perhaps he would go to the Rest House outside the station —it had neither lights nor furniture but neither was it haunted by the spectre of a vanished past.

It was not a porter but the waiter who came at Satadal's call. He stood expectantly but Satadal took no notice of him. Instead he walked up to the door and peeped out. The fine rain blew into his face. He came back into the room and stood by the table. It was as if he was immersed in thoughts of the past. Perhaps he felt that it was stupid to be so disturbed. It would be sheer cowardice and a confession of weakness if he ran away from the waiting room at the sight of this woman.

The waiter was still waiting for instructions. Satadal pulled a chair to the table, sat down and ordered tea. In the other corner of the room, Madhuri took off her cashmere coat, placed it on the bench and sat down.

Satadal Dutt and Madhuri Roy were today only two passen-

gers waiting for their trains in the waiting room. Today there
was nothing else between them. Indeed for the last five or
six years they had been strangers. This had not however
always been the case. There were days when they had not
been apart; in fact almost for seven years they had been man
and wife. When they first met, she was Madhuri Mitra, a fine
looking girl and a friend of his elder brother's wife. It was an
April day at Ghatshila and the forests were full of the fragrance of flowers and honey. Their intimacy began on a sudden
afternoon when Satadal saw her bathed in the light of the
setting sun as she stood in the mahua grove.

There is no doubt that they were soon deeply in love. Their
love was legalised and their names joined in the marriage
register. It did not however last more than seven years. By
mutual agreement, they again went to court and separated.

It seemed that both had realised that there was no longer
any life in their love. When they felt that they were drifting
apart, they did not wish to keep up the pretence and parted.
The love which bloomed one fragrant spring among the groves
of Ghatshila did not last seven springs. How was it that
their love disappeared when it was out of love that they had
married?

Yet there was no doubt that the bond between them had
snapped. Satadal felt it bitterly on the day when he was
putting his things together with undeft fingers while Madhuri
sat in another room reading a novel. He was going to Bhuvnes-
war for a week in connection with his work. She did not come
even once to bid farewell to her husband. He had then felt
that the light which poured into the room through the windows
was a mockery.

It was not only that winter morning that mocked their love.
Equally cruel was a Sunday afternoon in the summer of that
year. Madhuri was all dressed up for their usual Sunday stroll.
Satadal was however absorbed in sketching a Chalukya temple.
He had forgotten all about their Sunday routine and was
not even aware that his wife had dressed for going out. She

gazed at the purple clouds in the western sky and found them meaningless.

Of such symptoms of declining affection, there was no end. At last they realised that their love was a thing of the past. Or did they think that they had never loved at all? Nobody can tell. Perhaps they could have known if they had talked frankly to one another.

Or was it a case of a new passion that cancelled the old April of Ghatshila? Perhaps the earlier Aprils had become insipid. Satadal and Madhuri suffered in silence and moved in opposite directions. They did not repent for what they had done nor did they blame one another. There could be no blame when either both were right or both were wrong. Their growing indifference was mutual and there was no forgiveness on either side. All this however was undeclared. When their estrangement became intolerable they parted without recrimination. They could no longer bear the burden of their unexpressed misery. Silently they wrote off seven years of married life through an application in the Civil Court.

Within a year and half of their separation, Satadal heard that Madhuri had married Anadi Roy, an engineer. Madhuri also read in the papers that Professor Satadal Dutt had again married. The bride was Sudhakana, sewing mistress in a Calcutta School.

These new marriages must also have been prompted by love. Whatever others might say, Madhuri knew she was happy in her new life. Satadal too was happy with Sudha even though there were people who made unkind remarks.

In the dead of this winter night, when fate brought together Madhuri Roy and Satadal Dutt in the waiting room of Rajpur Junction, it was hardly necessary for them to be excited. They had separated for good and put an end to their relationship.

But if the past was no problem, the present predicament was not so easy to face. Why should two lives be brought so close in a railway waiting room when five years ago the law had cancelled their right to share life? It seemed that their

sudden encounter was a mockery of faith, as improper as it
was intolerable. If instead of Madhuri and Satadal, any other
man and woman had met as passengers in the waiting room,
surely there would have been no such sense of constraint.
They would have exchanged a few formal words of common
courtesy. Madhuri Roy and Satadal Dutt were unrelated
today but how could they forget they had been man and wife?

The silence of the room and the burden of his thoughts
made Satadal doze for a few seconds. His eyes closed. When
he woke, he remembered it was a waiting room. His eyes fell
on Madhuri who was sitting on the bench with her face turned
toward the wall. Satadal however did not turn away his face.
He felt a strange curiosity to watch Madhuri unobserved though
he did not know what it was he wanted to see and, in fact,
what could there be novel in her?

And yet there was something new about her. He had never
seen Madhuri in such a fine sari of cloud-dark crepe with a
border flowing almost to the floor. In the past, when they
went out visiting, she of course put on a handloom sari which
rustled as she walked and shed the fragrance of *hasnu hana*
all around. Today, nothing was left of the fragrance or music
of her movements. She now stood like an image fashioned by
another artist. Satadal had never before looked at Madhuri
so intently and yet so furtively. Today he really had no right
to look at her and that was perhaps why he could not take
his eyes away! The more he looked, the more he realised that
she was another woman. Strange and new and a little hard,
the proper wife for an engineer!

Satadal shook off these disturbing thoughts and turned to
his own immediate needs. He opened his suitcase for his
towel and soap. He undid his hold-all and took out a pillow
and a bedsheet which he placed on the easy chair.

As for Madhuri, she had no need to look at Satadal directly.
She could see his image clearly in the mirror. Perhaps she
first did so not because she wanted to but because the mirror
was there. Perhaps there was also a furtive desire to look at

him unobserved. She watched him in the mirror and saw him take off his watch, wind it and place it on the table. She saw that it was not the watch she knew. The wrist-band was also new. It was black and she had never liked a black band. She saw that he wore a new ring. The pillowcase was coloured and embroidered. She knew that he liked white and plain things and never cared for colour or decoration. Madhuri realised that the sewing mistress had taken him in hand and changed all his tastes.

He picked up his soap and towel and went into the bathroom. It was a welcome chance and she could look at his things closely but what is it that she sought? She carefully inspected every single article but found nothing she could recognise. Everything was new. There was not the slightest trace of what had been five years ago. Perhaps it would have been better if she had not been so curious.

If Madhuri had now looked at herself in the mirror, she would have seen that her eyes were full of jealousy. Her fine eyebrows were curved in envy. Her eyes were however fixed on the three suitcases which were all open. The watch, the purse and the glasses were on the table. The flannel tunic hung from the bracket and its golden buttons glistened against the light. What sort of man was this who could leave all his things scattered so carelessly in a waiting room? It seemed to her that his trust in men was unnatural. Equally extraordinary was her concern about things that nobody had asked her to watch.

As he returned, Madhuri turned her face away but she could still see him clearly in the mirror. There was no doubt that he was much thinner. It seemed that the sewing mistress had hardly any thought for his health. Madhuri had not seen him for five years but she knew he was hungry. His face never looked so pinched unless he was famished.

Satadal was indeed hungry. He took out some food from a tiffin carrier and arranged the plates on the table. As he was sitting down to his meal, he suddenly noticed that he had no water. He took up a glass and made to move toward the corner where there was a jug.

Madhuri had never thought that such an incident would hurt her so much. Since she had not imagined it, she was not prepared. Shaken out of her indifference, she turned her eyes sharply from the mirror and looked directly at him. She was quite visibly annoyed, but this angry movement and the slight frown seemed to be more natural than the pose of indifference she had maintained so long.

"What are you doing?" she asked.

Satadal started as he heard the question and looked in surprise at her.

Madhuri burst out, "Surely the heavens would not have fallen if you had asked me for a glass of water?"

His face broke into smiles as he said, "Of course not."

She stood up and came forward to take the glass from his hand. Bidding him sit down, she fetched him water. It seemed she had escaped the burden of silence in the waiting room. His easy smile had broken the barriers between them. It was after all only a waiting room.

She placed the glass of water on the table and started to arrange the dishes. As her bangles clinkled against the glass, it seemed that memories which had slept for five years were suddenly revived. Who would say that they were two passengers who had casually met? One would think that they were man and wife and perfectly in tune with one another. He saw that her fingers were thinner, but she took up the food, as though with a prong, as skilfully as before. She stood by his side and their bodies almost touched. He could hear her short easy breathing in the silence of the room. One end of her sari had dropped on his arm but she hardly noticed it. It was nothing so unusual that one need observe it.

"This is all bazar food, I suppose," said Madhuri. Satadal did not miss the insinuation in her voice. He knew that she had always had a repugnance for such food. Half apologetically he said, "Yes, I bought it in the bazar at Katihar."

"Where are you going now?"

"I am going to Calcutta," said Satadal.

She asked again, "Do you still stay there?"

He said, "Yes, what about you?"

Perhaps it would have been better if their conversation had not taken this turn. Her hands trembled and she lost her sense of ease. It seemed that his question suddenly made her remember who she was. She moved away a little and softly said that she was going to Rajghat.

The topic ended there. There was nothing else to ask. They were passengers who had come by the same train but now they would travel by different trains along different routes. One would go to Calcutta and the other to Rajghat and yet in a moment of forgetfulness they had drawn rather close.

Perhaps in order to break the sense of constraint, Satadal asked, "You will then have to take the train for Patna?"

"Yes," said Madhuri, "You had better finish your meal."

It seemed that it required an effort for her to speak these words. However, she got them out and moved away. She remembered that she was waiting for the train to Patna. She could not stay indefinitely in this waiting room. She looked nervously at her wrist watch and went back to her bench.

The glass of water looked like liquid fire in the flash of the electric light. The food she had arranged neatly on the table also seemed full of hostility. Satadal again felt awkward and his feelings were tinged with a sense of shame. He blamed himself that he had run after an illusion knowingly.

He got up from the table and wrapped himself in his shawl. He reclined in the easy chair and lighted a cigarette. He could not touch the food, but did not understand why. In fact he did not even try to understand.

The waiting room was again nothing but a waiting room. Two strangers were counting the moments while they waited for their trains. But the trains were not yet due. Nor was there any sign of a third passenger. Someone at last appeared, but it was only the waiter. He had a tray with a pot of tea and two cups. He placed the tray on the table and left.

Satadal looked at the cup thirstily but turned his eyes away quickly as if he had seen a snake. The two cups on the table seemed to him a mockery of fate. He had not ordered tea for both. Why then had the waiter brought tea for two? No, it was impossible for him to take up the cup.

Madhuri did not look at him directly but she knew that he had not touched his food and it now seemed he would not take his tea either. How stupid of the waiter not to have poured out a cup of tea! But why should Satadal feel so shy? She remembered an old incident, but those days were for ever gone.

The two had gone to Madhupur to spend Christmas with her uncle. It was on the very first day of their visit. He said nothing but spent the whole morning in the garden without taking his cup of tea. The reason for the silent protest was that tea had been served by a servant and not by her. When this was found out, everyone in the house was upset. They all scolded Madhuri. Even her brother, when he heard the story, said, "When you know that Satadal likes you to serve, why did you send the servant?"

Tonight, they were in a waiting room. It was neither Christmas nor Madhupur nor her uncle's house. Nor was it proper for Satadal to turn his face away and sit silently like an offended husband.

Yet Madhuri could not remain indifferent. It seemed that the scene in the waiting room, like a scene in a well acted play, vividly reminded her of his habits and temper. She almost felt that Satadal had the right to complain. No one could scold her today for not serving him, but she heard a voice within bidding her do her duty. She realised she must also play her part.

"Why are you not taking your food," she asked. Her voice was tender and persuasive.

"I won't take these things so late in the night," replied Satadal.

"At least you can have some tea."

"That is a good idea, but what about you?"

There was a suspicion of a smile on Madhuri's face. "It was not a part of the contract that I should take a cup," she said.

Satadal smiled shyly and said, "Perhaps not, but since the waiter has brought two cups, why not?"

They both turned grave for a moment. It was truly not the waiter's fault. It seemed that there was a tinge of regret in what she said. Perhaps she meant to say that it was not the fault of the waiter, but of their fate. Otherwise, why should they suffer this embarrassment on this rainy night in a waiting room after five long years?

Perhaps she found it impossible to keep on sitting in silence. Perhaps she willingly submitted to the conspiracy to which the waiting room itself seemed a party. In any case, she moved to the table and poured out the tea. She did it with the same old skill and grace. Satadal got up from the easy chair and placed a chair next to his.

Madhuri sat down quietly and found nothing to object to. They both realised that the waiting room at Rajpur was bringing them together. Neither had the heart to check the course of events. When Madhuri sat down beside Satadal, it looked a picture of perfect conjugal life.

Satadal sipped the tea and sighed in contentment. Surely, it was not merely the taste of the tea but because he felt in it the touch of Madhuri's hand.

He smiled, "You looked so grave that I was feeling uncomfortable."

Madhuri also smiled. "For you it was only a slight embarrassment but I alone know what I felt."

"Were you frightened?"

She lowered her face and said, "Yes."

"What was there to fear?"

Their conversation had begun on a light note, but his last words were heavy with an unexpressed sadness. Her words were full of regret. His words had a tone of assurance and intimacy. The past was past. Why should one fear or regret it?

It is easy to judge the dead with sympathy and understanding. We also tend to think of the good qualities rather than the faults of those who are no more. Madhuri and Satadal could look back on their past with sympathy. The fear, the hatred, and the suspicion of the past had been burned up and scattered. Today they remembered the past like the sky of one long night lit up by a thousand stars. It was hard to believe that it was a lost horizon. It would not have been human if they had not longed to capture the spirit of the past. Madhuri looked at Satadal and said, "You have lost a good deal of weight."

"What if I say the same thing about you," said he.

He pointed at her fingers and said, "Why have they become so thin?"

Madhuri was about to hide her fingers in her sari, but in a mood of forgetfulness, he took both her hands and warmly pressed them. Madhuri did not object.

He looked at her face as if he was seeing her anew. "There has been no change in your face, no change at all," he said.

Everything has changed, only not her face. All their past life was cancelled, but the face he had loved remained the same. How could it be? Was it mere fancy or a trick of the eye?

Madhuri blushed deeply. Not like a maiden at the first address of love, nor like a shy bride meeting her lover for the first time in a bridal chamber. She blushed like a wife who had met her man after long years of separation but was sure of her husband's love.

It was not a bower, not a bridal chamber. It was not the house of a newly married pair but the waiting room in a railway station. They were only two passengers but they sat as if they were passengers in the journey of life and had never separated.

As they finished their tea, she asked, "Where is your uncle?"

"He has built himself a house in Dehra Dun and stays there."

"And what about Puti?"

"Puti? She has grown up and married. You remember Romesh. He now has a job in Delhi. He married her."

Her hands were still clasped in his. It seemed he was afraid to let her go. After a long search, he had discovered an image which was lost five years ago. With both his hands, he held her lest she disappear again.

"Could you believe me, Madhuri?"

"Believe you? Why not?"

"I have not forgotten you. I can never forget you."

"It is nothing strange. I can see you have not forgotten."

"But what about you? Have you forgotten me?"

Madhuri closed her eyes.

It seemed she wanted to withdraw within herself before she could reply. Her head reclined a little toward Satadal. There was a suspicion of tears in the corner of her eye.

He drew her closer to him and insisted, "You must tell me, Madhuri; I will not let you go till I have a reply."

Suddenly Madhuri started as if she had felt the touch of fire. She released herself and stood up. A bell rang loudly and shattered the silence of the winter night. Even the mirror on the wall was trembling. It seemed as if the waiting room was protesting against the impropriety of their conduct. A passenger train had just entered the platform.

Madhuri rushed frantically to the door as she cried, "He is coming by this train."

The man who now entered the waiting room was Anadi Roy, Madhuri's husband. His face lighted up with joy as he saw her, like the face of a lonely traveller who had just discovered an inn.

Madhuri's face also lighted up but there was still a touch of sadness in it, like the smoke of a lamp that has burned too long.

Anadi Roy noticed it and asked in an anxious tone, "Are you feeling all right?"

"Yes, I am quite well."

"You had to wait for a long time. Is it not?"

"Yes."

"I could not help it. The trains nowadays never run to time; otherwise I would have been here at least two hours ago."

Anadi Roy started unpacking to make things comfortable for his wife. As she protested, he only took out a fine shawl, wrapped her in it and said, "You better rest for a little while. You will feel much better."

Satadal was watching them from his chair. He could not stand the scene and got up hurriedly. He walked up to the door and looked out. He returned and rearranged his things. The sight was indeed intolerable for him. The fine shawl clung to Madhuri's body in loving embrace. How proud and happy Anadi Roy looked! To Satadal it seemed that Madhuri was a woman of ancient legend to be won by prowess. Satadal felt like a defeated candidate who could only look helplessly on the scene. He could of course walk out of the room but he still lingered for an answer to his question.

Anadi Roy looked at his watch. It was almost time for their train. Madhuri put on her coat. The porters reappeared on the scene and announced that the train for Patna was coming in.

Madhuri stood by her husband. The porters collected the luggage and started to go out of the waiting room. Satadal feared that there was little hope of getting an answer to his question. It seemed to him that Madhuri had locked him in a house of lac and set it on fire.

Were their seven years of joint life a mere illusion? Was it so easy to forget? Does legal separation so irrevocably divide the heart? Madhuri would never answer that question.

Perhaps it would have been better if with a smiling face she had gone off with her husband, but she did tarry for a moment. The porters had already gone out of the room, but Madhuri paused near the door. It seemed that the bond of past affection held her steps. She turned to Satadal and smiled as she said goodbye. Satadal could not smile. Wounded affection and vain claims throbbed in his heart, but there was no

time to give expression to them. He only wanted an answer to
his question. He said, "Of course you will go, but you have
not answered my question."

The smile on Madhuri's face faded. She looked at him in
surprise and asked, "What question?"

Satadal repeated, "You did not tell me if you have really
forgotten me."

Madhuri kept silent. Perhaps she had forgotten. Yet how
was it possible that she could forget a question asked seven
minutes ago when memories of seven years were so vivid to
her? Satadal was puzzled.

Madhuri said, "I must go. It is getting late."

Satadal winced as if her words were like a blow. He remembered that Madhuri had to go and could not be stopped. For
seven years, he had made her wait but today he had no right
to keep her waiting even for a moment.

Sadly he said, "Then you won't answer my question?"

Madhuri replied gently, "It is a question which should not
be answered."

"Why?" asked Satadal.

Madhuri said, "It is an improper question."

Satadal got up from his chair and said, " I see." He turned
his face away and said almost rudely, "Go if you will, but
why did you make this show?"

Satadal's words were ungracious. For a moment Madhuri's
face became hard. Her eyebrows curved in anger. She brooded
for a moment and then her face again beamed with smiles.
She looked at her watch and said, "Come and visit us at Rajgir
with Sudha."

Satadal was taken aback and said, "And then?"

"I shall come to see both of you off when it is time for you
to depart."

"Why?" asked Satadal.

"You will then get an opportunity of paying me in my own
coin."

Madhuri smiled and added, "Why, I would perhaps be as

angry as you are today. Perhaps I will ask equally foolish questions."

For a few seconds, Satadal looked vacant.

Then he burst out laughing and said in a loud voice, "Yes, I now understand."

Satadal looked at his own watch. Even though he did not turn to the door, he knew Madhuri had left. The house of lac had not been set on fire. Instead, laughter seemed to be echoing from end to end.

Rajpur Junction suddenly came to life. There was the siren of an incoming train, the train for Calcutta, which entered the platform on the opposite side. Satadal hurried away toward it.

The two trains would move away in opposite directions. Rajpur Junction would become dead and silent after this momentary burst of life. Soon there would be no trace left of the strange encounter between two casual passengers.

Signs of their meeting were however still evident. There was a tray on the table with two empty cups on it. Before the Junction went to sleep again, the waiter would take them, clean them and place them on the cupboard. Perhaps he would place the two cups at two ends of the shelf.

K A Z I   N A Z R U L   I S L A M

Thieves and Robbers

Who calls you a robber, my friend? who calls you a thief?
All around the robbers beat their drums and thieves rule.
Who is the Daniel that sits in judgment
                                    over thieves and robbers?
Is there any in the world that is not an exploiter?
O Supreme Judge, hold high your sceptre,
For the great are great today only by robbing the weak.
The greater the robbery and theft,
                            the cheating and exploitation
The higher the status in the modern world of nations !
Palaces rise built with the congealed blood of subject peoples,
Capitalists run their factories by destroying a million hearths.
What diabolical machine is this fed by human flesh?
Live men and women go in but come out like pressed
                                                    sugar-cane.
The factories squeeze the manhood out of millions,
And fill the millionaire's cups of wine and jars of gold.
The moneylender grows pot-bellied on the food the hungry
                                                        need,
The landlord ruins the poor man's home to drive his coach-
                                                    and-four.
The merchant mind has turned the world into a brothel
                                                    house,
Sin and Satan are its cupbearers and sing a song of greed.
Man has lost food and health and life and hope and speech,
Bankrupt, he rushes toward sure destruction.
There is hardly any way of escape,
For all around are trenches dug by the greed of gold.

The whole world a prison and robbers are the guards.
Thieves have their brotherhood, cheats their comradeship.
Who calls you a robber, my friend? who says you steal?
You have only taken a few coins or cups,
But you have not stabbed man in the heart !
You are not inhuman though you may be a thief,
Like Ratnakar,[1] you can still become Valmiki if only you
                                        meet a real man!

[1]Ratnakar was a notorius robber but through contact with a holy man
was converted and became Valmiki, the first and most famous of Sanskrit
poets who composed the *Ramayana*.

Partings

I

We could no longer deny that we must part at last.
I knew for certain that the eager ship
With tautened coils sighed sad but impatient for the voyage.
I stood on the sunlit deck beneath the open sky
And saw the distant shore slowly fade away.
Dim grew the shape of men and women on the quay
Who looked with steady gaze so long as eye could see.
A song of parting dimmed the bright light with tears.

With denuded eyes I looked at you in helpless pain:
A figure of grief standing on the quay
Flowers in your idle hands and eyes empty of all thought.
The blue waters surged up in cruel mockery.
Through my tears I saw your tired face
Grow dim and fade away in the distant sky.

II

I returned and saw your long-limbed body stretched
On the old familiar bed in the old familiar room.
The old familiar smile still lingered on your lips
The bright red sari still nestled to your form.
I saw your right arm limply flung across the bed
Disobedient locks curl upon your brow
Your clothes still atremble with your gentle breath
Only the peerless eyes were closed as if in sleep.

Suddenly I felt my heart stop its beat.
Suddenly my world lost all its beauteous smile.
I saw the writ of death on the earth's dry bones.
Suddenly I knew that never again would you
Stand close to my heart and lift your face
With fearless eyes and gentle smile through all my days.

III

Those who stood close to you and were dear—
You will forget them in the flow of time, my friend.
Life's uneven road curves in and out
And suddenly they disappear beyond the bend—
Disappear as suddenly as first appeared.
Perhaps the darkness of the night swallowed them
While you came marching across the night.

Those who were once dear are today
Only faint memories of the mind :
Bodiless and immaterial phantoms of the heart.
The feeling dead leaves dry and rotting bones
But love cannot live on fond regrets.
If old love has now become a shadow of the past
Better dark oblivion hide it in darker shades.

ARUN MITRA

The Song of the Harvest

Leaves of the spring and summer storms
Make me eager and expectant.
The murmur of falling rain
Or the morning music of autumn permeates my being.
The village in the late winter
Brings a strange music to my ears.

Whenever I touch the earth I feel
I have returned to my old world.
In your body I seek the throb of growing roots.
In my embrace the vastness of the world narrows down.
The expectancy of your lips thrusts up with the urge of life
In a thousand hints and suggestions.
A suspense hangs over all my world.

When we whisper softly to one another
Its fragrance fills the entire world:
The distant horizon comes near in my hopes.
When I look at your face
I believe that words can be full of life like flowers.

We are people of the land of rivers.
Its heart is wide open to us
And to it we return.
That is why I love you.
Here we can be intimate like the spreading turf
Or like the gentle rain.

Here we can conquer the fear which dries the sap in the roots,
The rigours of the desert which dry up the clouds
And become one with the future.
All strangeness and familiarity we tread beneath our feet
Even our sufferings make rich the days.
In vast rivers we float our songs
The plains thrill and burst into music.

We seek to drown ourselves in the depths of our eyes.
We want to renew ourselves like the harvest.
Sometimes underneath the evening star
Sometimes in the early dawn when the birds awake
Sometimes in the midday in the deserted house
I draw you to me and push aside all whispers from outside.
In deep human love
I deny the memories of a failing past
I call on you to blossom like a new twig.
I say:
Be like the sheaves of new corn
The flowers of the golden mustard.
I say:
Embrace me in your deep murmur.

NARENDRANATH MITRA

The Thief

AMULYA got into the room, took off his scarf and threw it on the bed. Taking a box of soap and a pot of cream from his pocket, he held them out to his wife. "Take these and put them away."

Renu put out her hand and then hurriedly withdrew it as if she had touched a snake. Looking her husband in the face she said, "Why have you done this again?"

Amulya averted his eyes, but next moment he looked sharply at her and with a strange smile in which anger and irony were nicely blended, he said, "I have brought them to sell in the market."

Then he changed his tone and snarled, "I say, will you take them from my hand or not?"

Renu said calmly, "If you can take them in your hand, I suppose I can take them in mine."

She took the things and put them on a teapoy.

Amulya said, "Since you know you must accept them, why can't you accept them decently from the start. Why all this pother—this parade of honesty? And besides, why should I repeat what I said in jest one day. I have bought these things with my hard-earned money."

Renu looked at him and smiled sadly, "Please do not lie to me."

Amulya flew into a rage, "No! I must not lie to you—I suppose you are my father confessor!"

Renu was amused, "Shouldn't one speak the truth before anybody else?" she asked.

Amulya looked at his wife with admiration. Her smile was

so sweet. If only she were free from this touch of puritanism, this bit of extra honesty!

Renu looked down for a moment and then raised her eyes and said, "I say this for your own good. If you are caught red-handed, what will happen then? How can you keep your honour?"

With unshakable self-confidence, he replied, "Are you crazy? Do you think I am a novice?"

A M U L Y A was not ashamed to brag that he was no novice. Renu felt she would die with shame. It was a fact that he was a practised hand. He had no scruples. She recalled an incident a few days after their marriage. They had gone in a tram to the Eden Gardens for an outing. They were sitting side by side on a bench, talking. The conductor asked for the fare, but Amulya seemed absorbed in conversation with his wife. When the conductor repeated, "Your ticket, sir?" with a nod of the head, Amulya continued to talk. Renu noticed that the conductor moved forward with a cynical smile. Amulya was talking nineteen to the dozen, but Renu blushed with shame. Who knows what the conductor thought? And all for the sake of a paltry two annas!

When the conductor had moved some distance away Renu whispered to her husband, "Why haven't you paid the fare?"

Amulya smiled and said, "Ah, you noticed that, did you? Why should I get into the first class if I wanted to buy my ticket?"

Renu was amazed. She said: "O dear, can a gentleman with a lady get into any other class but the first? Is that any excuse for not buying one's ticket?"

With pride in his voice, he replied, "Even when I travel alone, I travel without a ticket; the more so today when you are with me. Marriage is an expensive affair. If I cannot make up a little in this way, how shall I get on?"

Renu thought Amulya was joking. But when on the return

journey he became serious again at the sight of the conductor and, giving the man a nod, began to talk to her, Renu's heart was beating fast. What a mercy it was not the same conductor! Had it been so, the fellow would not have let Amulya alone, but would have realised the fare. What shame and disgrace! They would have lost face and been disgraced before a whole tramful of men.

Getting off the car, Renu said, "Fie upon you! I don't like such things at all!"

Amulya replied, "What things?"

"To ride a tram or a bus without a ticket."

Amulya laughed, "You have been seriously thinking of that, have you? What a prig you are! I see you will give me no end of trouble. You are not suffering from hysteria by any chance, are you?"

"What do you mean?"

"I mean, women of this type have such fits."

Renu said, "For shame! to save a paltry two annas—"

Amulya interrupted her, "Not two annas, but twice two annas—four annas, the price of a packet of cigarettes!"

"Why didn't you tell me? I'd have given you the price of a packet of cigarettes."

A N D another incident a few days later. Amulya had brought a costly comb.

"Have a look at this. Isn't it lovely?"

Eagerly she stretched out her hand for the comb, saying, "Isn't it splendid? What's the price?"

Amulya said, "Two and a half rupees."

Renu changed colour. "Why have you spent so much on it?" she demanded. "I have plenty of combs. Only the other day, at the bride's party I got three combs as presents. I don't like spending on such flashy things. Is there any sense in throwing away money like this in these hard times?"

With a complacent smile, Amulya replied, "Are you off

your head? Do you think I'll spend my hard-earned money on luxuries? After all, Pal Brothers do not pay me so hand-somely, do they?"

Renu said, "Have the Company sold it cheaply because you belong to their staff?"

Amulya said with a smile, "They have given it not cheap, but absolutely free. They know after all that a brand new bride has come to my house."

Renu said bashfully, "There! Don't talk nonsense. Honestly, tell me what rebate they have given you. I'll buy one for my sister-in-law."

Amulya at once flew into a rage, "Shut up! As if you do not understand! A woman's naivete may be pleasant sometimes, but not always."

"What do you mean?"

"It means I haven't paid a penny for it. I have got it through sleight of hand. If I could do it for you, it does not follow that I can do it for your sister-in-law as well."

Renu was dumbfounded. Then she said, "I don't care to have this comb. Please return it tomorrow. For shame!"

"There! it puts you into a temper instantly. All right, you'll get one for your sister-in-law also. After all, she is the wife of your brother."

But for a long while, Renu did not say a word.

T H I S time also, Renu remained silent. It was unthinkable how any gentleman could behave in this way. Her people—her father and brother—were poor, but could even their worst enemy accuse them of touching other people's property, let alone stealing it?

The thought of her ill-luck brought tears to her eyes. Why was she fated to get such a man for a husband? She had now to live all her life with this man, love him and share all her joys and sorrows with him. And then, though children would be born to them, Amulya's tastes and habits would not change, because age did not change such habits, nor money; they died hard. She had seen much and heard still more. Then it would be all in the day's work. Nobody would know that Renu was made of different stuff, that she could not tolerate such things. Would anyone believe her? Everyone would think that as Amulya was a thief, so was Renu, for was she not a thief's wife?

In the dark, in the close embrace of her husband, her whole body shrank in shame. She was clasped by a man who was small, whose tastes were low, and who felt no shame nor scruple in pilfering things. She remained still for a while when he kissed her and then softly said, "Will you promise me something?"

"What is it?"

"Do not bring things in this way any more. Honestly, I do not need them at all. I do not want anything except that you should become a good man, a decent man. I'd be happy if others knew you for a gentleman."

Amulya turned away. He would have no peace, he said to himself, till he had taught her a lesson and paid her back fully in her own coin.

Renu said, "There, you are angry! I said that only for your own good."

Amulya replied, "I too speak for your good. Go to sleep in peace."

NEXT morning, Amulya got up and called his wife, "Look here, listen—"

Renu came near him and said, "Yes?"

Amulya whispered, "Hasn't Binod Babu of the upper flat brought home a set of brand new bell-metal cups yesterday?"

Renu was surprised, "Yes, but how does that concern you?"

"You are very friendly with Binod Babu's wife. You have access to her rooms."

"Yes, the lady is very fond of me. Her youngest son will not eat unless I serve him."

In the same whispering tone, Amulya said, "That's rare good luck! After feeding the baby, you can easily lift the cup under the cover of your sari."

Renu was terribly shocked. "What nonsense are you talking? Are you off your head?" she cried.

Amulya was unabashed. "Not in the least," he said. "Do you know the price of bell-metal these days? If you can lift a few of the cups, we can go to the theatre and see a play from the box." Amulya laughed.

Renu replied in an angry tone, "Your joke is as bad as you are ! I can't stand such jokes."

Amulya said, "I am not joking, honestly."

At noon, when she was feeding the baby in the upper flat, Renu's hand trembled. What a horrible man was Amulya, how monstrous his jokes!

A F E W days passed. It was 7.30 in the morning, but Amulya was still in bed. Normally, by this time he had finished his tea and left home. He was on duty in the shop from 8 a.m.

Renu drew the blanket from his face and said, "Well, sir, aren't you sleeping too much today? Isn't it getting late?"

Amulya smiled in a strange way, "No, it won't be late today."

The manner of his speech and the smile made her heart beat fast. She said, "What's the matter? Is the shop closed today? What's the occasion?"

Amulya flared up, " 'What's the occasion?'—As if you don't know. The occasion is my funeral."

He turned his back on her.

Looking fixedly at him, she said, "I knew it would come to this."

"What's that you said?" asked Amulya.

"What's there to be said? Yet what luck they did not hand you over to the police."

Amulya said, "Alas, the pity of it ! But perhaps it would

have been better if they had handed me over to the police. I should have served my term in prison and you could have lived with an honest man for a change."

A short while after, he thought out a plan and got up. Returning from his wash, he saw Renu was sitting with her head on her knees.

Amulya came near her and said, "What's the matter? Why are you sitting like that? What's wrong?"

Renu made no reply.

Amulya said, "Have you made up your mind not to show your face? I thought it was I who must hang his head in shame, not you !"

This made her look up. She said, "Have you no grain of feeling in you? Have you a heart of stone?"

But Amulya was not stony-hearted. He ran his fingers over her hair softly and in silence.

After a minute, Renu looked up again and asked, "What crime did you commit that they sacked you?" It was as if she was demanding an explanation not from Amulya but from his employers. Amulya was a bit surprised. He said, "The old cashier plotted against me. My crime was that I could not steal a tin of powder for his wife. He poisoned the ears of the manager against me."

Renu believed him. She said, "Yes indeed! I know them all—they are all honest, aren't they?"

F o r a few days, Amulya was busy in search of employment. He had hopes, but none materialised. Renu gave him encouragement, "Why worry so much? There's no want of jobs, these days. You will get one eventually."

But in a few days, the stock of rice in the house was exhausted. Not only rice, indeed all food ran short—pulses, oil, salt, everything.

One day Amulya had an idea. He said, "I can do one thing; you won't mind, will you?"

"Why should I mind?"

"Then give me the pots of cream and the boxes of soap. I have acquaintances who will buy them at a fair price."

Renu's face darkened. She said, however, "All right, take them. But you can't go on like this for long."

Amulya replied, "That's true, of course. We have to tap other sources too."

A few days later, Amulya brought home a costly fountain pen.

Renu looked at the pen and then at her husband. Amulya feared every moment that Renu would scourge him with her tongue. But, strange to say, she did not say a word. As if nothing uncommon had happened. she continued to sweep the floor. Only once she raised her head to say to her husband, "The cocoanut oil is finished and not a drop remains."

Amulya replied, "That's all right."

By evening, the pen had vanished and instead, the room was filled with rice, pulses, oil, and coal. A bottle of scented cocoanut oil was also there.

This time also, without a word, Renu stored the things when Amulya said, "Wait a minute. There's another thing for you."

Renu said, "What is it?"

Amulya took a pot of Oatine Snow and gave it to Renu saying, "I have bought it for cash from Pal Brothers. I held out the five rupee note before old Bistu Babu's nose and said, 'Change please, I am in a hurry.' "

With a smile, Renu said, "How funny you are, you remember everything!"

In the dark of the night, Renu nestled against the hairy bosom of her husband and said softly, "It gives me the creeps. Is it good to be so foolhardy?"

Pressing the coil of her hair softly and lovingly, he said, "Is courage not good? If I had no courage, we would have starved by now. It would have been all up with us if I had been timid like you. You are completely useless. If only I had your opportunities!"

Hurt by his word, she could not speak. Her lips trembled. She felt she could not rest till she had made him eat his words.

Two or three days later, the opportunity came, but her hands shook and her heart beat fast. Binod Babu's wrist watch was hanging from a nail in a corner of the wall. It hung like this quite often. Binod Babu was absent-minded; moreover, he would get flustered when he was late for office. One day he would leave his pen at home, and another day his purse.

With a blanket over her, the lady of the house was sleeping like a log. Renu fed the baby, rocked it to sleep and put it to bed. Stillness reigned in the house. The ticking of the watch seemed audible even from a distance. Strange, wasn't it, that tiny watch ticking so loud! No, it was the sound of *her* heart beats. Once she tried to get out of the room. But it was impossible, she had not the strength to move. Her feet seemed rooted to the spot and the two tiny hands of the watch appeared to hypnotise her.

But if she was caught, if the watch was missed and the search began? But then how was she concerned? She had been coming and going here, talking and gossiping for the last six months. Could anybody ever say that even the smallest article was missing?

When somehow she managed to reach her own room, her face was flushed with a strange excitement. Her heart was beating high and her breathing was quick. Rapture was never so great. She touched the small watch once again with her fingers. Was even the first touch of a man so intense, so thrilling?

IN THE evening, Amulya came back home, sad and depressed. He had not got a chance today. As he set his eyes on Renu, he started in surprise.

"What's the matter? I see you have dressed up today."

She bolted the door and then, coming close and clinging to her husband, said in a sweet and affectionate voice, "Why this envy? You will also dress up today, though only for a short night. But even one night is not insignificant."

Somewhat annoyed, Amulya said, "Don't talk in riddles. Tell me plainly what you mean."

Renu said, "Wait a little, dear. Why are you so restless? You men are always in a hurry. You can't hold your soul in patience."

After dinner, without putting out the light, she stretched herself by the side of her husband.

Amulya was surprised, "Will the light remain on all night?"

Renu smiled and said, "What harm is there, if it is on all night? No, dear no, it won't be on all night, it will be out presently. There now, hold out your left hand, please."

"What will you do with my left hand?"

"I need it for a minute."

Slowly she took out the small watch, band and all, from inside her blouse and put it on her husband's wrist, "Let me see how it fits."

For a moment, Amulya gaped with wonder. Then he said drily, "Dear me! Where have you got it from?"

From a high mysterious plane, she smiled softly and said, "That's none of your business! Tell me if it fits well."

Then all of a sudden she left the bed, put off the light and returning, clasped her husband's neck. Tonight she had no shyness, no diffidence, no sense of worthlessness. She had conquered the world.

"Well, darling, why are you silent? Tell me, doesn't it fit you well?"

It should have indeed! She had become his real helpmeet. All these days Amulya had been looking forward to this. He should have been in the seventh heaven of bliss. But clasped in the warm embrace of his wife, Amulya still felt numb. It was as if all the sweetness and beauty of the world had vanished and the two familiar arms that were clinging to his neck were no longer the slim, braceleted hands of a beautiful young woman. Alas! they were stained and had lost all their grace.

PREMENDRA MITRA

The Rats

The rats roam about in the dark.
Throughout the livelong night
Breathless they run
And pant as they stop
With trembling hearts and wide open eyes:
Embodied fragments of small and unimportant fears
Scattered and driven all around
Charged with life but cast with the shadow of death.

All through night I hear in the dark their pattering feet.
They rob field and store in weak but eager greed.
They carry in their teeth fragments of the night back to
                                                    their holes.

And yet once upon a time
The marvellous morn
Had sent its call to them
With the eager horizon lit with golden light.
The vast plain had throbbed
To the music of the wings of flocks of birds.
They also looked up with timid eyes.
But with hurrying fearful feet
They sought the safety of their holes.

Their dim shadowy minds
Are fearful with the darkness of the night.
They store up in the dark their revolt against life.
The light brightens with the endeavour of the day:
The rat holes of life still remain empty and dark.

Where the River Meets the Sea

I

You could draw up your knees and somehow crouch, but you could not sit straight inside the boat. The moment you raised your head, you struck against the roof.

Dakshayani was fat and suffered from gout.

She could not sit in one posture for long without stretching her legs. But it was not that discomfort that worried her just now. The reason why she was lashing Lakshman with her scathing tongue was quite different.

There was no doubt that what Lakshman had done was extremely wrong. But however angry at heart, few dared to offend the man who was in charge in this journey to a strange place of pilgrimage. Even though herded like cattle under the low roof of the boat, one had to bear with it without a word of complaint.

But Dakshayani was not the person to hold her tongue. Widowed in her childhood, she was known for her sharp tongue and high spirits. People feared her even more for the valour of her tongue than they respected her for her extraordinary devotion and meticulous performance of religious rites and duties.

Though her sole support in this pilgrimage, even Lakshman did not escape her tongue. She was no respecter of persons. Besides, she had good reason to be angry.

"Luckless, burnt-faced monkey! Once let us get back home

and I'll break your head with the broom, or I am no daughter-in-law of the Mukherjee's."

Lakshman made no answer. Indeed, these few days, he was hardly to be seen, far less heard. He avoided Dakshayani scrupulously and stuck to the platform over the rudder which was beyond her reach. He had not the nerve to appear before her in her present mood.

From within the cabin, her voice came, "Cheat, rascal, son of a pig. If I am indeed a true daughter of a Brahmin, you will not survive the journey. Before you reach the sea you will die of cholera."

Lakshman started at the curse, but he had no heart to protest. Her anger related to those who had been making a din, sitting on the open deck on the other side of the boat. Even Lakshman felt now that he should not have done such a thing for money. But now there was no help.

Again a clamour arose from the cabin. A small, pretty girl of about eight stood at one end of the cabin, and the noise centred round her.

Though sweet to look at, the tiny tot had a precocity of manner and speech that made one's blood boil. The women in the cabin were protesting with one voice, "There's not an inch of space and yet you want us to make room for you."

Her delicate face distorted into a grimace as the little girl said with a wave of her hand, "Why not? You have not bought this boat."

The ladies were aghast at her cheek; "Good Lord! Do you see her manners?"

One said, "No wonder, if you remember her birth." The girl twisted her little face and said, "No more lectures please! Make way like good people, or I'll walk over your bodies."

Dakshayani had remained silent till now. Purple with anger and with eyes flashing fire, she said "You dirty, impertinent hussy! Just pass over our bodies, do, and I'll throttle you and bury you under the earth."

But she was not the girl to be frightened, not even by

Dakshayani's bloodshot eyes. With an insolent stare, she pouted her lips and answered, "Pooh! bury me indeed!"

From the other side, a woman called out, "Why are you picking a quarrel with them, Batashi?"

In the twinkling of an eye, Batashi burst into tears and cried, "Mummy, I wanted to go to Lakshman dada and the slut tried to throttle me."

The women in the cabin were astounded: "What shame! Who on earth throttled you? And she calls her a slut!"

Batashi sobbed and cried, "No, I musn't call her a slut! I must remain silent even if I am throttled!"

"I say, why are you throttling my little girl?" said Batashi's mother. As she came in, the ugly story of her life was writ large on her unhealthy face. Her eyes were sunk deep in their sockets and it did not take long to recognise her for what she was. She came near, took Batashi in her arms, and said, "Which one throttled you? Tell me, which one?"

Without batting an eyelid, Batashi pointed to Dakshayani and said, "That fat slut."

Even Dakshayani was tongue-tied for a few moments at this shameless and false accusation. Then, with a great effort she checked herself and said bitterly, "If I had throttled you, you would have gone to heaven. Could you have such rare good luck?"

It is difficult to say how fierce the quarrel would have grown had not the boatmen intervened and forcibly separated Batashi and her mother from the rest. Though a long-range battle of words continued for long, it did not degenerate into a violent free fight.

Such rows had been a daily occurrence since the boat left Diamond Harbour. Ever since Dakshayani had come to know that a party of prostitutes had been taken on the boat, she had not taken a drop of water. If she could have, she would have left the boat.

Only twice during these days had she taken any food. It was when the boat had anchored and she could get down and bathe to wash off the pollution of being in the same boat as these women. For the rest, she went without food, taking not even a sip of water. All the other passengers belonging to the upper classes were women and most were, like her, widows. But they could not practise such self-restraint. They consoled themselves with the thought that, on the sacred waters of the Ganges and in a wooden boat, the rules could be somewhat relaxed. But this did not convince Dakshayani, and she held fast to her austerities.

Fasting was all in the day's work with her and she did not mind. The only compensation she allowed herself was to haul Lakshman over the coals. But today she appeared somewhat fatigued. That a chit of a girl should humiliate her seemed to have broken her spirit. With excited voice the other women were discussing the minx and her future life of disgrace.

"Did you hear her—and she not yet out of her swaddling clothes!"

"She has such venom in her young fangs, God alone knows, when she grows up, how many families she will ruin."

"That mite of a child, our granddaughter's age; Lord! How she lies! She would even turn day into night!"

"Who knows why mother Ganges bears such sin."

But Dakshayani did not take any part in this discussion. She even forgot to abuse Lakshman.

T w o more days passed. The night was dark and foggy and the shores were not in sight: You could hear only the gentle lapping of the current against the boat. Sky and water were all one mass of darkness; only the dim light from a few boats moving toward the sea gave an idea of the size of the river.

Unlike the others, Dakshayani could not sleep. The only person awake, she was looking through the chinks of the cabin and gazing at the black water. Suddenly, it seemed to her that the gentle murmur of the water was changing into a muffled roar. When the boatmen had cast anchor in the evening, she had overheard them say that the tide was very strong here and there might be a disaster if the boat were not properly handled.

She became frightened. Was it the tide after all? But the boatmen were all asleep. If anything happened!

The roar of the river was steadily growing. She was wondering whether she should wake the boatmen when, with a deafening noise, the boat heeled over.

The tide pulled out of its moorings a heavily laden barge and dashed it against Dakshayani's boat. Its boards cracked with a loud report and the river was full of the cries of the frightened crew and passengers who were rudely awakened. Dakshayani was stunned and hardly aware of herself for some moments. When she came to, she realised that she was swimming in the cold water of the river. She could see indistinctly in front their battered boat entangled with the black shadow of the huge barge.

The rudder was broken, the floor of the boat had split and it was sinking.

In her youth, Dakshayani had learned how to swim. She found that she could keep afloat without much effort. The crew of the barge were rushing about and making a great din. She called out to them but apparently they did not hear her.

At her age, she could not hope to keep afloat for long in that cold water. Besides, she had heard of the crocodiles of the Sundarbans—how long could she escape them?

Then luck favoured her. The rudder of the capsized boat was floating by. As its black shape loomed large in the dark, she screamed in terror, but the next moment she saw that it was wood and she clasped it with all her might.

But she was startled as her hand touched something soft like a bundle of clothes.

A frightened cry also came from the bundle.

As she drew near and looked carefully, everything became clear. Her scared, piteous eyes wide open, Batashi was clinging fast to one end of the rudder. Even at that terrible moment, the horror of having touched her made Dakshayani's hair stand on end. The crew on the barge had lighted some torches and were looking for the drowning pilgrims. Dakshayani saw the face of the helpless girl in the indistinct light but felt no touch of pity. In fact she felt her fury rising as she thought that this chit of a girl would like a venomous young snake one day grow up and poison the world.

Batashi's tears and her efforts to cling to the rudder did not move Dakshayani at all. She pushed her off into the water with all her strength.

"Mother," cried the girl piteously as she slipped from the rudder. She swallowed some water, raised her weak hands in a vain attempt to hold on to Dakshayani and sank. The black waters of the river glowed for a moment in the dim light of the torches. It seemed the curtain of silence had dropped on her last cry.

But that last choked cry of the girl turned everything upside down inside Dakshayani. She could not bear the scared and piteous appeal in the eyes of the girl before she sank. Dakshayani no longer remembered that the girl was a harlot's daughter with the blood of sin coursing in her veins. Nor did Dakshayani care any more that if Batashi lived she would not only sin but also suffer. She thought that she could still see Batashi's clothes on the water. Perhaps the girl could still be saved. In her own exhausted state of body and mind, Dakshayani could not let go her hold on the rudder. Torn between hesitation and conflict, she grew excited.

Suddenly, not far off, the girl's head appeared for a moment on the surface.

Dakshayani plunged forward, groped in the water, but her hands were stretched in vain. She could feel her limbs, weak with fasting and gout, becoming numb. Still she made a last attempt—she even had a feeling that she had clutched something, but by then she was completely exhausted. The rudder was still within her reach. She tried to stretch her hands and seize it, but they did not move. Only the thing she had seized remained in her benumbed grip.

II

B U T it was not her fate to die in an accident. As she came to, she heard some people talking, "It's not for nothing that people say there's nothing like a mother's love."

Exhausted and dazed, Dakshayani could not take in the import of the remark. Nor did she feel any interest in what they said. A feeling of deep exhaustion came over her, and she again dozed off. But by the morning she was almost normal.

It did not take her long to understand that she was lying in a cabin in a ship. Through the small window at the right, she could see the sun rising. It rose with bloodshot eyes from the mass of water which stretched from horizon to horizon. She knew that she had been rescued but could not remember who had saved her nor how she had come to be aboard the ship.

An unknown boatman came to her, all smiles, and said, "Mother Ganges is very kind. If we had been a little late, neither of you could have been saved."

Presently more boatmen crowded near the door. "The kid had swallowed so much water that we had no hope of her recovery. You must be full of virtue, for, otherwise, your child could not have been saved."

The old boatman added, "The mother held her child so firmly that it was difficult to unloosen her grasp."

Another rejoined, "Won't she hold her tight? After all it is a mother's love."

Somebody picked up the girl and put her on Dakshayani's lap, saying, "There's your girl, mother, she is now all right."

Dakshayani had been listening to them in silence, but now her surprise knew no bounds. They had taken the prostitute's daughter to be hers and put her by her side!

The girl was terrified and would not lift her eyes. Dakshayani was shocked and said, "But she is not my daughter."

All the boatmen laughed. The old man said, "You are right, mother. She is a foundling, we have picked her up from the water of the Ganges. What do you say to that, girlie?"

The girl hung her head in confusion. Dakshayani felt scared at this turn in the boatmen's talk and repeated in an earnest tone, "But she is *really* not my daughter."

Who would listen to her words or notice the expression on her face? Batashi pressed her face against the bed and started sobbing. The old boatman pulled her up by the hand and said, "What a crazy girl you are? Why don't you see the joke? Why don't you too say, 'You are not my mother either?'"

Dakshayani was at her wit's end and gazed at these men with a bewildered look. She did not know how they had got this strange idea into their heads nor how she could disabuse them.

Batashi sobbed and went out of the cabin, holding the hand of the old boatman. Tired in body and mind, Dakshayani stretched herself and closed her eyes; she wanted to turn over the whole thing in her mind.

Dhablat was not far off. By afternoon, the boatmen dropped her there. They had to turn in another direction and could not take her any further in their boat.

The old boatman was very polite. He bade goodbye and said, "There are strict orders, or I should have taken you up to Gangasagar (i.e. the estuary of the Ganges). But you will get any number of boats from Dhablat sailing to Gangasagar. Take one of them."

Perplexed, Dakshayani walked down the wooden gangway to the shore.

The old man called out from behind, "Please mother, hold the hand of the girl, the wood is slippery." Like an automaton, she held Batashi's hand and reached the shore.

It was all a matter of hours but such a storm had blown through Dakshayani's mind that it was no wonder she looked bewildered. The boatmen told her that but for one or two of the crew in her boat, probably no one had survived. Her companions, who had come from the same village had all been trapped in the cabin and died a tragic death. With all their efforts, they had failed to save any but the two of them. She had tried several times to rid them of their idea that Batashi was her daughter but in vain. They had seen her plunge from the broken rudder into the water to save the girl; and how could they believe that anybody but a mother would do this? The old man had said with a smile, "Blood is thicker than water, mother; it can't be concealed."

The boatmen drew back the gangway and sailed off. For a long time after the boat had gone, Dakshayani remained standing in an absent-minded manner with Batashi's hand in hers. Then suddenly she remembered and violently threw off the girl's hand. For all the hardships and the accident attending her journey to Gangasagar, her sorrow and anger fell on the girl.

Ignoring Batashi completely, she went ahead. She was absorbed in her own worries. True, she had her travelling expenses, for she had tied her purse to her waistband and it had not been lost. But how could she, an unaccompanied woman, get back home, far less go on to Gangasagar? She was indeed at sea.

She saw in front a crowd of men around a few big houses. She made toward them in the hope that they would make some arrangements for her. Suddenly she heard a thud behind her and stopped. Batashi had been following her all along and now she had stumbled against some broken tiles.

Dakshayani was about to scold her but she restrained herself when she saw that Batashi had cut herself badly against a sharp tile. Blood was gushing from the wound. Dakshayani felt she had to take her hand and lift her. Scared and tearful, the girl hung her head. She was after all a kid and had almost drowned only two days ago. She was still very weak and, after her fall, could hardly stand. Dakshayani took her hand, and saw that her legs were trembling.

Full of anxiety, she asked, "Can't you walk?"

Whatever her faults, Batashi was no fool. She fully realised her utter helplessness. She also sensed the difference between the kind of women she knew and ladies of genteel family. She had insulted Dakshayani only two days ago and was now completely at her mercy. Her only hope was that Dakshayani should take pity on her and she was afraid of annoying her.

In a choked voice, with her head lowered, she said she could walk. But as she limped behind Dakshayani she felt giddy after a few steps and was about to faint when Dakshayani caught hold of her.

Now there was nothing left for it but to carry the girl. The thought of holding Batashi in her arms revolted Dakshayani and she could hardly bring herself to do it. She had felt sorry for the girl when she fell but now she was filled with disgust at the prospect of touching a harlot's daughter. Who knows, she argued in her mind, that the girl had not pretended to faint? She shook the girl in an effort to wake her, but Batashi had really fainted and was limp in Dakshayani's hand. Dakshayani had perforce to take her in her arms. At every step her mind rose in rebellion, questioning God's justice. What sin had she committed to suffer this pollution?

As Dakshayani laboured under the burden, some men hurried forward to help her. Dakshayani told them in brief the story of the wreck and asked for their help. She made no fuss about Batashi now. She had realised at last that it was useless.

One man took the girl from her arms and said, "You must nevertheless thank God that He has not separated mother and daughter. What a calamity it would have been otherwise."

A merchant gave them shelter for the night in his shop. It was decided that the next day they would be put on a boat going to the sea.

It was cold, for it was the month of Paus. Whatever warm clothes they had were lost with the boat. The merchants took pity on them and provided them with a mat to spread on the floor and a rug. They thought that this would protect mother and daughter against the cold.

It was a mud hut with thatched roof. The walls were made

of reeds and the cold winter wind blew through the chinks.
A kerosene lamp from a corner threw a dim light. Batashi sat
in one corner and shivered in the cold. She was weak and
sleepy, but she dared not come to the bed. She remembered
the disgust she had seen in Dakshayani's eyes when she came
to after her fit. Nervous and terrified, she looked longingly
at the warm bed, but she would neither speak nor move.

Dakshayani too was feeling cold, but to use the rug meant
asking the girl to share it. She found it hard to reconcile herself to the idea of sleeping in the same bed with that unclean
girl. The moments dragged. Dakshayani realised that there
was no way out. She called Batashi and said, "What's the use
of sitting there and shivering? Come to bed, will you?"

Batashi knew that there was no affection in that bidding,
but she was so sleepy and tired that she was grateful for this
small mercy. She crept timidly into a corner of the bed, pulled
the fringe of the rug over her and lay down.

Dakshayani threw the entire rug over Batashi and said in a
bitter tone, "Why this pretence? I won't touch the rug. Put
it properly over yourself."

Batashi drew the rug a little more but could not spread it
well over her body.

Dakshayani sat brooding over her fate. It was cold and
grew colder with the passing hours while a storm raged in her
mind. At last she could keep up no more and decided to lie
down in one corner of the bed. Batashi was by now fast asleep.
Dakshayani kept as far away as possible and put one end of
the rug over herself. She thought to herself that she would
bathe in the Ganges and wash off the sin of associating with
this girl born in sin.

Soon she was enveloped in deep slumber. When she woke
in the small hours of the morning, she was surprised beyond
measure to find that Batashi was nestling close to her and
had laid her hand lightly on Dakshayani's neck.

The kerosene lamp was still burning. Dakshayani looked
at the face of the girl in the dim light. It was pure and serene.

She could not imagine how such soft and lovely lips could utter the filthy words she had heard. Batashi's face had absolutely no suggestion of a future Jezebel.

Dakshayani could not easily forget her lifelong habits and beliefs. She was about to push away Batashi's thin white hand from her neck but a strange sense of pity overcame her and she found she could not do so. She lay still and the girl nestled close to her heart.

When Batashi opened her sleepy eyes, the first thing she noticed was that the blanket had been spread neatly over her. Dakshayani was standing near the door and doing something. Batashi was stiff with fear. Perhaps she had occupied the bed and monopolised the blanket. Perhaps Dakshayani had had to sit awake all through the winter night. As these thoughts struck her, she was about to jump out of the bed, but Dakshayani lifted her hand and said, "Stay where you are! You need not get up in the cold."

She paused for a while and added, "Stay in bed till I return. You needn't be so afraid."

Full of surprise, Batashi again lay down. The unexpected note of affection in Dakshayani's voice brought her to the verge of tears. She hid her face against the pillow and tried in vain to suppress her sobs.

Soon Dakshayani came back. She had brought rice crispies and some cakes. She smiled and said, "You are very hungry, aren't you? Get up now. Wash your face and have something to eat."

She accompanied the girl to the door of the hut. There was a pond nearby. She pointed to it and said, "Look, there's the pond. Can you go alone or shall I come with you?"

"I can manage," said Batashi.

Dakshayani cautioned her, "Step with care, will you? The bank is very slippery."

III

In the afternoon, they found a boat going to the sea and boarded it.

In the meantime, Dakshayani had bathed in the river and boiled some rice and pulses. She did not of course let Batashi touch the cooking vessels but their relations were now easy and they could talk to one another without constraint. Batashi sat a little way off from where Dakshayani cooked and talked freely. She did not like chillies, she said and added wisely, "Size doesn't matter, does it? The smaller the pepper, the sharper it is."

Dakshayani laughed at her and said, "One has only to look at you to know that what you say is true."

Batashi hung her head and did not speak.

Dakshayani's sari was still wet as they sat down to eat. They did not sit together but a little apart. This did not however stop their talking a great deal.

Batashi asked, "Don't you feel cold in your wet clothes?"

Dakshayani said with a smile, "Even if it is cold, how can I help it? You are not going to give me a new sari?"

Batashi said, "But I have also lost all my clothes in the river."

"If you hadn't, you would have given me one, wouldn't you?"

Batashi felt too shy to say anything. But presently, she rattled on, if only she had had her nice striped sari on, it would not have sunk, besides she had a real silk sari at home etc. etc.

As she talked, Dakshayani was again and again reminded of the background of Batashi's life. This made her feel uncomfortable, but her revulsion against Batashi had largely worn off.

There soon came a jolt in these happy relations. They were beings from different worlds who had been thrown out of their orbits. Encouraged by Dakshayani's attitude, Batashi was gradually losing her timidity and reverting to her old habits.

As they were getting into the boat, Batashi suddenly swung her neck and twisted her face in a pert and coquettish way that was hardly in keeping with her age. She also spoke in a manner that jarred on Dakshayani's nerves. "I can't get on to a boat again," she said, "water is an eyesore to me." And she burst into a cheap and vulgar song. But she could not finish. The words stuck in her throat as she saw the look on Dakshayani's face, and she grew pale with fear.

In a moment, Dakshayani's face had become very hard. She frowned angrily and walked straight into the boat with quick strides, without turning her face once to see if Batashi had also got in.

Perhaps she was cursing herself. It was not strange that the real nature of a young viper should show. What was strange was that, knowing everything, she had, only because the girl had a sweet face, forgotten her old aversion to such creatures.

The vulgarity of the girl's behaviour had set Dakshayani's teeth on edge. Who knew what she had seen and heard? The sins of many men and for many years had corrupted her young mind. Dakshayani felt disgusted with herself when she remembered that she had smiled at and talked to the little slut. To her shame she realised that she had developed an affection for the girl!

She remembered the pure, spotless record of her people. Her father and her father-in-law both came from high-bred virtuous families. She felt that her weakness for the girl was an insult to their memory and she silently sought their forgiveness. She swore that, as soon as she reached Gangasagar, she would cut off all connections with the girl.

Crestfallen and unhappy, Batashi moved round her to draw her attention. Her eyes were brimming with tears and she could not speak. But Dakshayani took no notice of her.

Batashi did all she could to make Dakshayani relent. It was a big boat but the only people on board were the two of them and the crew. The boat carried many dolls and toys of clay for a shop at Gangasagar.

Batashi looked at the dolls shyly and said, "I have a partridge like that but mine is bigger."

Dakshayani gave no sign of having heard her. She lay still with closed eyes. It was not clear whether she was asleep or awake.

Batashi tried again. In a tired voice she said, "This boat is very big. Big boats do not sink, do they?"

Dakshayani still made no reply.

Batashi made one last attempt. "I can massage legs very well," she said and placed her hand on Dakshayani's leg.

Dakshayani moved her leg away and said, "Don't touch me."

Batashi drew away her guilty hands and sat silent and tongue-tied. Her heart was heavy, for she did not know how to win back Dakshayani's favour.

There was a lump in her throat, but she bravely struggled to suppress her sobs. She felt she was choking. It would have been some relief if she could weep aloud, but she dared not lest Dakshayani became still more angry. But she could not restrain the silent tears that flowed down her cheeks.

Gangasagar is not far off from Dhablat. There was a favourable wind and the boat arrived quickly. Only a small part of the estuary had to be crossed. But Dakshayani had no idea that, after passing so far without any trouble, danger would crop up here of all places.

She had been lying down in silence since she got into the boat. As she approached her destination, she was compelled to get up and ask the boatmen about things, including arrangements for her stay at Gangasagar. She would not have been worried so much if she had been alone. But this girl had also to be provided for.

The girl followed her like a shadow but Dakshayani was determined not to take any notice of her.

As the boat approached the sea, it started rolling. She did not understand this change and came out of the cabin to ask the boatmen. Suddenly the boat lurched and she felt it slipping from under her feet. Batashi thought she was going to fall into the sea. With a wild scream, she clasped Dakshayani and clung to her. The older woman was also pale with fear and cried out loudly. Convinced that the boat was sinking, she gathered Batashi in her arms and held her fast.

Had not the boatmen got hold of her, nobody knows what she might have done in panic. Almost by force, they pushed them into the cabin and told them that there was nothing to fear. It was quite the usual thing for the boat to roll when the sea waves dashed against it.

But Dakshayani was not assured. She pressed the girl to her bosom and kept on repeating, "Better let us get off somewhere. We would rather walk."

The boatmen tried to impress upon her that there was nothing but water on all sides. Even if they approached the bank, it would only be forest land, infested with tigers. To get off meant certain death.

It was all in vain. With every roll of the waves, Dakshayani kept on saying, "Take all I have and let us get off. Let it be forest, let it be jungle but at least it will be solid earth. We shall somehow walk home."

When the boatmen found she would not listen to reason, they were annoyed and returned to their work.

Pale with the fear of death, Dakshayani sat pertified in the cabin. She seemed hardly aware that Batashi was clasped to her bosom.

At last they arrived at Gangasagar. The police and volunteer arrangements were good. Though she had none to look after her, she did not have any difficulty about anything. She rented a small hut built on sand and thatched with reed mats.

Now that the pilgrimage was done, Dakshayani grew more and more worried about Batashi. The girl had no doubt turned over a new leaf. Perhaps her link with her past was not strong. The ease with which she had forgotten all her past and adapted herself to her new conditions made it easy to think so. Seeing them together, who could say that her association with Dakshayani had not been lifelong?

Dakshayani did not notice it when Batashi started calling her Mummy. In fact she almost took the address for granted.

Early one dawn, Batashi got up even before Dakshayani.
"You are still asleep" she said. "Didn't you tell me that something was to be done today before sunrise?" Hardly awake,
Dakshayani did not reply. Batashi shook her and said, "Mummy dear, do you hear?"

Dakshayani turned on her side and said, "Are you crazy?
It will be hours before the sun rises. Come back to bed."

After a while, she put her hand on Batashi's body and
started, "There! the blanket is wet with dew. You aren't wet,
are you?"

"No, dear, no! Why should I be wet? Didn't you put a gunny
underneath before I went to bed?"

Dakshayani felt relieved and said, "Then lie down and sleep."

But Batashi did not want to sleep any more. She protested,
"This gunny and blanket weigh some fifty pounds. How can
I stand so much weight? Everybody is up. Let us also get up,
Mummy."

The bed was warm and cosy. Dakshayani could not bring
herself to come out of the warm bed and said, "Don't you
hear? It's raining. Let the rain stop."

Batashi exclaimed, "Who says it is raining? What you hear
is dew dripping from the roof."

It was indeed so. The roof as well as the walls of the shed
were made of reeds. The heavy dew of the winter night had
soaked through and was dripping on the sand.

Dakshayani had at last to get up. In a voice full of mock
seriousness, she said, "It seems you will gather all the merit of
Gangasagar and leave nothing for anybody else."

Batashi blushed and said, "Why are you laughing at me?"

Their stay at Gangasagar was drawing to its end. Soon, they
must return home. Dakshayani could not decide what to do
with Batashi.

Batashi had become very dear to her. She no longer denied
that she loved the girl. All the same, she knew quite well
that she could not take Batashi home with her.

Dakshayani would not tell a lie. It would be impossible for

her to hide Batashi's origin, but to take with her a harlot's daughter would be to humiliate her people. Even if others did not suspect the truth, how could she knowingly bring into the stainless family circle a girl born in sin?

No, she must give up Batashi. The question was how. She knew nothing of people who looked after orphans. Even if she had known, how could she be sure that Batashi would not come to harm? Her worries made her distraught. Batashi would speak to her and get no reply, or Dakshayani would get into a rage and say, "Don't bother me. Can't I get a moment's peace?"

Batashi would say nothing, but her eyes would fill with tears. Soon, Dakshayani would be full of repentance for her temper. She would take Batashi out with her, show her sights of the fair and tell her stories till she smiled again.

Dakshayani did not know what to do. Why should Batashi be her headache? She was a girl born in sin. It was sheer chance that threw her in Dakshayani's way. It was after all only a casual encounter. Why need she accept the tie for ever? If Dakshayani had not been there, surely Batashi would have found a place in the wide, wide world. If Dakshayani left her today, she would not remain uncared for. As for the quality of the shelter, after all what was the point of being too finicky for one born and bred in sin?

IV

A s Dakshayani pushed her way through the crowd one day, she had a sudden thought. She would just drop Batashi and go away. There could be nothing wrong in discarding a girl who was unknown a few days ago and would be a stranger a few days hence. This would be the easiest solution.

When she reached a relatively open space she suddenly noticed that Batashi was missing. She had seen the girl a few moments earlier but now there was no trace of her. The foolish girl was really the limit, she thought. Unless you watched her all the time, she would gape at whatever she saw and be left behind.

Dakshayani stood for a while and waited, but Batashi was not to be seen. Now she was really angry. She had again and again asked Batashi not to let go her hand on the street. In an unknown, unfamiliar land, even adults may lose their way. Rows of huts stood on all sides. They were all alike and you could not tell one from the other. If the girl was lost, it would be difficult to find her.

Dakshayani moved about but there was no sign of Batashi.

Now she was worried. Who knows which way the foolish girl had gone? She could certainly not find her way alone. She could not even ask anybody. The huts were called after the names of the boatmen and she did not know the name.

Dakshayani called out loudly, "Batashi!" but there was no response. She advanced farther and asked whoever she met but in vain. She became more and more worried.

At last, Batashi was found. After a long and lone wandering, Dakshayani noticed a crowd of people near a shop. As she pushed through the crowd, Batashi, who had been crying her heart out, rushed to her and clung to her.

All Dakshayani's fear and suspense now turned into anger. She smacked the girl sharply and said, "Didn't I tell you not to let go my hand? Will you again go by yourself?"

The people around pleaded for the girl, "Don't beat her, please. The girl has cried her eyes out."

One person said, "But what a foolish daughter you have, mother! A grown-up girl, she cannot give the name of her people. She could only say, 'I've come with my mother'!"

But Batashi did not mind the smack at all. She hid her face on Dakshayani's lap and said with a tearful smile, "Why did you go ahead without me?"

When Dakshayani came back to their hut, she asked, "Well, what if I had left you and run away?"

Batashi raised her large, trustful eyes and replied with a smile, "Nonsense!"

That night Batashi would not eat anything. She had caught a cold and her eyes were swollen. Dakshayani felt her body and did not press her to eat.

The thatched roof did not shut out the cold at night. To keep Batashi warm, Dakshayani bought an extra blanket, but she found that the child's temperature had risen.

Batashi's condition became worse in the morning. She was delirious with high fever. Dakshayani was frightened out of her wits.

A kind neighbour called a doctor from the welfare centre. The diagnosis made Dakshayani still more nervous. A hard case of pneumonia! The girl must be removed to hospital. Dakshayani had a lifelong distrust of hospitals and would not at first agree.

The doctor explained that careful nursing and constant medical care were essential if Batashi was to be saved. These could not be arranged except in the hospital. If she wanted to save her daughter, she must agree.

Dakshayani had no option but to agree. The doctor assured her that there was no reason to fear. She would not be permitted to stay with Batashi, but she could go and visit her whenever she liked. And the doctor would see that she had every attention and care.

When Dakshayani came out after putting Batashi into hospital, she felt numb in body and mind. It was the day for holy bathing. Countless pilgrims hurried to the mouth of the Ganges. She too moved with the crowd but like an automaton. She felt nothing mattered. A wisp of a girl, unknown till the other day, had in a few days' time changed the whole course of her life. Customs, tradition and religious ritual had lost all meaning for her.

Today, Dakshayani need not look back at every step to see if Batashi was following. Nobody pestered her today with unending questions. Today she was free from worry on Batashi's account. There was no need to keep a careful watch. Batashi would not now dip her head too many times in the water, nor go into the river beyond Dakshayani's reach. Nor would she annoy other bathers by throwing up water in her vain attempts to swim. Dakshayani could now perform her religious rites undisturbed, but all these gave her no pleasure.

After she had finished her bath Dakshayani felt a little calmer. As she thought over the matter she felt that, however deep her love for Batashi, perhaps she should not grieve if the girl died. She would in any case have parted from the girl in a few days. Who knows to what depths of sin and misery the helpless girl might sink in a cruel world? If God gathered the girl to Himself while she was yet young and pure, who was Dakshayani to protest?

Yes, Batashi had better die. Living meant no end of misery and sorrow for her.

So Dakshayani reasoned, but her heart rebelled against her intellect. When she returned after her bath, her hands were full of dolls and toys for Batashi.

As the day advanced, Dakshayani grew more and more restless. None but God could understand her mental agony.

Yes, Batashi had better die. And yet Dakshayani's whole soul grieved that she was dying. Unknown to her, her world had started to revolve round this little girl.

Long before sundown, she got up. Her longing for motherhood—perhaps the oldest of all instincts and stronger than all religion—swept away all the barriers put up by custom and convention. She poured out her heart in prayer for the life of Batashi. She repeated to herself again and again that if Batashi lived she would gladly accept any censure and disgrace that an unfeeling world might impose. If her husband's family repudiated her, she would go back to her father's family or fend for herself. "Only," she prayed to God, "let Batashi live."

She was disgusted with herself that she could have thought that Batashi had better die. As she walked, all sorts of ideas came to her mind. What was the proof that Batashi was born in sin? She had heard that prostitutes often kidnapped small

girls of good families. Who could say that Batashi was not a
girl from a respectable family? Had she not come from a
good family, she could not have changed so much and so
quickly. Dakshayani could no longer tolerate the idea that
Batashi must suffer all her life for an offence she had not
committed. She was resolved that she would not go back
alone. She would take Batashi with her and face all the conse-
quences.

A big tent had been pitched as a hospital for the pilgrims.
Dakshayani went round it a number of times but could not
summon the courage to ask about Batashi. Who knew what
was in store for her? Her heart beat fast in fear and suspense.
At last, with great effort and much fear, she asked about
Batashi.

The young man took all the particulars about the girl. "You
want to see her, don't you? Wait a minute, I'll go and inquire."

With palpitating heart, Dakshayani waited. A long time
passed, but there was no sign of the young man. She grew
extremely restless. She regretted very much that she had
listened to these people and agreed to send the girl to the
hospital. The doctor had said that she would have no difficulty
in visiting her. Why then should there be this delay? Her
distrust of hospitals grew. They might not have nursed Batashi
at all, who knows? Perhaps they had neglected her. Perhaps
no one was near to give her water when she was thirsty.
Dakshayani was beside herself with anger, sorrow and suspense.
She felt like tearing the curtains open and snatching Batashi
away by force. Batashi would survive without their medicine.
She felt exhausted by the long waiting. Suddenly she saw the
young man coming toward her along with the doctor.

Even before they reached her, she knew. She stood still as a
post. Her face was expressionless and dead but there was
immeasurable pain in her heart.

The doctor mumbled a few words. They did not reach her,
nor did she need to hear them.

Before he had finished speaking, she had turned back and

was about to leave. She did not want even to have a last look at Batashi. The doctor walked a few steps with her and said gently, "We need your help. The cremation of your daughter will be done by us, of course. But we need a few particulars."

Dakshayani turned round and said drily, "Particulars?"

"Yes, her age, father's name etc."

She remained speechless for a while. Then this daughter-in-law of a proud Brahmin family forgot her lifelong tradition and training and did something which must have shocked all her prim and self-righteous ancestors in their correct heavenly abode but brought the deepest joy to the unseen God of life and love.

Dakshayani said, "How can you expect me to utter my husband's name? Let me have a piece of paper. I'll write it down."[1]

---

[1]It is a grievous sin for a Hindu wife, according to old tradition, to utter her husband's name.

S A I L A J A N A N D   M O O K E R J E E

The Obstacle

I T   H A P P E N E D just before the autumn holidays. May be
it was the last week of September or perhaps it was
early October. The frogs no longer croaked in the little ponds.
The fury of the monsoons was over. The cloudless sky was
as blue as ever. The night was still young and the moon rode
in the sky. The white light had flooded the veranda of my
bungalow. I was stretched on my easy chair while idle thoughts
flitted through my mind.

Idle thoughts indeed! I was a servant of the coal-mines. No
one could be sure when and what danger threatened. Besides,
the mine whose Manager I had just been appointed was not
at all in good condition. The programme of pillar blasting was
in full force. Santal coolies demurred to go down because of
the threat of gas.

I am writing about a time when mining laws were not so
strict as today. There was an urgent demand from the head
office that I must send more coal. I had sent down a group of
Santals. They would blast one or more of the pillars with
dynamite. We would collect the coal the next morning.

There were some sephali trees just in front of my bungalow.
They were covered with masses of white flowers. The powerful
scent hung in the air and turned my thoughts astray. I remembered another autumn evening in the days of my youth
when also the sephali had bloomed.

Even the memory of those days was sweet. I was in pleasant
reverie when suddenly the headman rushed frantically in. A
man had been killed in one of the lower galleries of the mine.

In a moment I forgot the sephali-scented autumn night. I

233

forgot all about my vanished youth. I took up a safety lamp
and said, "Let us go."

I T W A S a Santal youth who had died. He was healthy and
handsome but those who work in coal-mines often die sudden
deaths. His death was sudden but not unusual.

In this case, however, he had almost courted death. One
could even call it suicide.

I would of course have to send an explanation. There will
however be no trace in our records of the reasons for his death.
New deaths would soon make us forget him.

They say that if a man dies for a woman, it is material for a
story. This young man had died for a woman. I have therefore
kept a brief record of the facts. If in future some writer could
tell the story and make our Paltu of Mainabuni mine immortal,
it would perhaps be the proper thing.

I H A V E never come across finer men than these Santals.
They do not know how to tell a lie. If they commit a fault,
they admit it with a readiness which astonishes us. Whatever they do, they do with gusto. They drink and get drunk.
They sing and they dance. They make merry. They also work
untiringly from sunrise to sunset. Whether in work or in play,
they recognise no restraint. They know how to kill but they
also know how to die.

Near the mine, there was a huge mango garden with a dozen
houses built under the trees. We used to call them the Santal
quarters. Poltu had his room in these quarters.

One day, I was walking past the garden in connection with
some work. Poltu suddenly stood in my way. I asked, "What
is the matter?"

Poltu said, "Come once to our quarters, Mister."

I asked, "Why?"

Poltu said, "Jhuman has returned."

I said, "What am I to do if Jhuman has returned?"

Poltu said, "You won't have to do anything, Mister. Please only come with me."

I followed him into the garden. The winter was over and there was a suspicion of spring in the air. The trees were covered with mango blossoms. Many-coloured butterflies were flitting around. The newly arrived cuckoo poured out his heart in song. I was walking on when Poltu suddenly stopped and said, "Look."

I followed his finger and saw that not far away a Santal girl stood under a tree. She was humming a tune and putting mango blossoms in her hair.

I asked Poltu, "Who is she?"

Poltu smiled and said, "She is my wife."

I forgot myself and kept gazing at her. She was really worth looking at. I have seen many Santal girls but I have never seen anyone like her. She was as beautiful as she was full of life. She was of course dark, but till I had seen her I had never known that a dark girl could be so beautiful. It seemed to me that a master artist had carved a woman out of black marble. She was flawless. As she stood under the tree, I suddenly thought she was a goddess of the forest. Poltu said, "Do you know, Mister, why she is standing there?"

I said, "No. Why?"

Poltu said, "She is waiting for Jhuman."

I was not listening to him. In fact, I could not turn my eyes and was looking at her with wonder. When Poltu said, "I tell you, Mister, I shall kill this Jhuman," absent-mindedly I replied, "Why?" but immediately collected my thoughts and said, "Oh, is that so?"

Perhaps she had heard our voices and turned her face. Her laughter rang out but, like a frightened doe, she ran away. Poltu asked, "Can you hear the flute, Mister?"

I had in fact been listening to the flute for some time. It seemed to me that someone was sitting by the side of the hillock and playing a most plaintive tune.

Poltu said, "Jhuman is playing on his flute. The fellow starts to play and Kinni runs out of our house. She has no heart in her work once she hears the flute."

I asked, "So your wife is called Kinni?"

Poltu said, "Yes, Mister; you have just seen her."

I confess I wanted to see Kinni once again.

"Call Kinni, I shall give her a scolding," I said.

Poltu rushed away to call Kinni. I stood alone in the mango garden. After a few moments Poltu returned but he had with him not Kinni but a Santal young man. He had a wonderful body and excellent health. This was Jhuman, with a reed flute in his hands.

I asked, "Where is Kinni?"

Poltu said, "She refuses to come."

Jhuman used to work in the mines but had suddenly left us.

I asked him, "Hallo Jhuman, where have you been all these days?"

Jhuman replied, "I have been here and there and everywhere."

I felt it would not be proper to ask the question in the presence of Poltu. I called Jhuman aside and asked, "Why have you returned?"

Jhuman said, "I could not help it. I felt I must see Kinni."

I scolded him and said, "This is very wrong. Kinni is Poltu's wife. You had better leave her alone."

Jhuman did not say anything and only smiled.

I asked, "Why don't you reply?"

Jhuman breathed out a deep sigh and said, "I will run away with Kinni."

"But why should Poltu let her go?"

Jhuman said that he would carry her away by force.

"But it won't be right. Don't you realise that?"

Jhuman said, "I am a Santal. I do not understand all this."

I asked him, "Does Poltu know?"

Jhuman said, "If he does not, call him and tell him what I want to do. If he can, let him stop Kinni and me."

I asked in a low tone, "So Kinni is in love with you, is it not?"

Jhuman smiled and said nothing. In spite of my repeated questions, he would not say a word.

I thought I would find out from Kinni. I called Poltu and said, "Better bring Kinni to my bungalow one day. I shall try to persuade her."

I THOUGHT that when Kinni came to my bungalow I would watch her carefully and ask her whom she loved. With whom did she want to live? I was still waiting when I heard after a day or two that there was a terrible row in the Santal quarters. I was worried and immediately got ready to go there.

When I arrived, I was astonished by what I saw. The men and women of the quarter stood in a large circle in one corner of the garden. In the open space within, Poltu and Jhuman were fighting. It seemed that two tigers were engaged in mortal combat. Muscles swelled on their bodies. Blood was flowing from Poltu's forehead. There was also a wound on Jhuman's knee but neither was prepared to give in. Entirely oblivious of the crowd, they were intent on fighting one another.

I turned to an old Santal and said, "Can't you stop them fighting?"

The old man waved to me to desist and said, "You better keep out of it."

I could not do so. Jhuman had attacked Poltu so violently that I feared that unless they were stopped, he might kill him. I passed through the circle, entered into the open space and shouted aloud, "Jhuman !"

Jhuman let his hands drop when he heard my voice. I had thought that this would end the fight but Poltu saw his chance. In a moment he had thrown Jhuman on the ground and sat on his chest. If I had not hurried forward, he would have strangled him. I separated them, but because of my intervention, Jhuman had lost. He therefore had to give up all hopes of getting Kinni.

If he did not get Kinni, life was not worth living. Jhuman was terribly depressed and in a few days disappeared. No one, in fact, had any news of him.

Poltu was happy at this turn of events. In his joy, he started drinking day and night. I was curious to know how Kinni was faring. Was she still quarrelling with Poltu? I could not however make enquiries about a common Santal girl, for I was the Manager of the mines.

I of course met Poltu now and then inside the mine. He was always dead drunk. If I asked him any question, he answered whatever came to his head. Besides, whenever he saw me, it reminded him of Jhuman and he started to abuse him in filthy language. His words were such that I had no option but to leave him as soon as possible.

Once during the rains, I had to go down into the mine one morning. When I came back about midday and was taking off my waterproof, someone called me from behind. I turned and saw Poltu. I asked him, "What is it you want?"

Poltu said, "I have come to you Mister, so that you may give Kinni a good scolding."

I asked, "Why?"

Poltu said, "She is behaving very funnily with me. She won't talk to me and she won't cook for me."

"If she does not cook, what do you eat?"

Poltu retorted, "I cook for her."

I was suddenly very angry with Poltu. I told him, "You are rightly served. I cannot blame Kinni if she does not talk to you or cook for you. You should deem yourself lucky that she stays with a drunkard like you. How can you expect it otherwise when you are dead drunk all the twenty-four hours?"

I abused him and asked him to get out but, before my words had ended, there was a peal of laughter from outside. I came out to see and found that Kinni was rolling with laughter. She followed me up the steps. She was as beautiful as ever. Her eyes were liquid and her figure full of grace. She had coiled her hair in a knot which rested on her right shoulder. The first time I saw her she had mango blossoms in her hair. Today she had a kadam flower with green leaves.

Poltu explained, "When I told Kinni that I was coming to you to complain against her, she accompanied me to hear your judgement."

I pretended to scold her, "This is very wrong of you Kinni. Why do you quarrel with Poltu?"

The answer was another peal of laughter.

This time I was angry. "Why are you laughing?" I asked.

Kinni retorted, "Do you want me to weep?"

I asked, "Poltu drinks too much: Is this not the trouble?"

Kinni said, "Not only does he drink but he abuses Jhuman day and night."

"Is that why you quarrel with him?"

Kinni could not stop laughing as she said, "Of course, yes."

I said gravely, "When Poltu again drinks and abuses Jhuman, you come and tell me. I shall punish him, but don't you quarrel with him."

Kinni laughed in Poltu's face and said, "Didn't I tell you so?" and ran away like a streak of lightning.

I felt a little sorry for Poltu. He had such a fine wife and was still unable to live happily. He was truly unfortunate. I told him, "Don't drink so much. Besides, since Jhuman has left, why do you keep on abusing him?"

I had not yet bathed or dined and dismissed Poltu. I could not however forget Kinni. Her image seemed to linger before my eyes.

W H A T happened next can be very briefly related. No one had thought that Jhuman would return. Poltu had gone to drink with his friends and Kinni was sitting alone in front of their house. Suddenly she found Jhuman standing before her. Her eyes filled with tears as she looked at Jhuman.

Jhuman said nothing but kept looking at her with sad eyes. It was Kinni who spoke first. She wiped her tears and said,

"Why have you come back after such a long time?"

Jhuman said, "I could not bear it any longer and felt I must see you."

"You could bear it very well till now."

"It was my fate. I tried to win you but I failed. I have made up my mind to die and that is why I have returned."

Kinni said, "Don't be foolish? Why should you die?"

Jhuman said, "I am telling you the truth. Look what I have here."

He showed her a stick of dynamite, a charge of gunpowder and a safety lamp. He explained that he was going down into the mine. After blasting the pillar, he would not move away. Tomorrow, everybody would know that he was dead.

Kinni pulled him to herself and clung to him. She pleaded with him, "Don't act foolishly, Jhuman." She started and broke away from his embrace when suddenly she heard Poltu. In the clear moonlight, Poltu shouted to her in a terrible voice. Without a word, Jhuman left her and walked away towards the mine. Kinni trembled but said nothing.

Poltu asked, "This was Jhuman, wasn't it?"

Kinni said, "Yes."

Poltu asked, "Where is he going?"

Kinni replied, "He is going into the mine."

Poltu said, "I shall finish him today. I will blow him up with dynamite."

He tottered away after Jhuman in a drunken state. Kinni could not remain alone. She also ran after them towards the mine.

POLTU signed the pay roll and drew out the stuff from the godown. This made him a little late but he did not mind. He had learnt that Jhuman had gone into gallery number thirteen. Poltu knew the mines in and out. He knew that this gallery had no outlet. If he could somehow remove one pillar near the entrance, the coal from the roof would block the way and

Jhuman would be buried alive. He laughed to himself as he thought of Jhuman slowly suffocating to death.

His calculations however went wrong. His joy at the prospect of Jhuman's death and the enormous quantity of wine he had consumed made him do something he had never wanted to do. He blew up a pillar all right but it was not the one he had meant to. A pile of coal came down and made him also a prisoner.

Poltu did not at first realise this. As soon as he heard the dynamite go off, he leapt with joy and shouted to himself, "Now you will die like a rat!" As he turned to go out, he discovered that he had blocked his own way out. He took up his safety lamp, but he did not know what to do. He found another lamp moving towards him and asked, "Who goes there?"

It was Jhuman who replied.

Poltu breathed a sigh of relief. "Perhaps this is all right. We shall go to our death together. It is better that both of us die. Look here, I have blocked the way out."

Suddenly, he heard a third person coughing in the dark. Poltu lifted the safety lamp and asked, "Is there anyone else in the gallery?"

Jhuman said, "Yes" and focused his safety lamp on Kinni's face.

Poltu started and said, "What brings you here Kinni?"

Kinni did not say anything but Jhuman replied on her behalf. He said, "I had made up my mind to die. Kinni followed me in order to make me change my mind."

Poltu said, "This is excellent. We shall all three die together."

The close confined space was gradually filling up with gas. Poltu coughed, Jhuman coughed and so did Kinni.

Suddenly, something stirred in Poltu's mind. He said, "I can clear a way out, but this time we will have to strike the dynamite with a hammer. Whoever does it will die. Who shall it be? You or I?"

Jhuman had made up his mind. Without a moment's hesitation he said, "I shall strike the dynamite."

Poltu laughed, "Why should it be you? Are you not in love with Kinni?"

Jhuman said, "Yes, but that is why I want to die."

"Be it so," said Poltu and placed the dynamite on the coal which blocked the way.

Jhuman lifted his hammer to strike at the dynamite when Kinni rushed up and caught both his hands. She said, "No, no, it must not be so. You must not do it, Jhuman. You let go the hammer. I shall strike the dynamite."

Poltu watched Kinni and Jhuman as they clung to one another in the face of death. What thoughts passed in his mind, he alone knew. In a voice devoid of emotion, he said to Jhuman, "If you have anything to say to Kinni before you die, this is your last chance. You can move away a little so that you can speak to her by yourself."

Kinni pulled Jhuman away and pleaded with him to desist from suicide. Their talk was interrupted by a terrible explosion. To their horror, they realised that Poltu had struck the dynamite. Kinni and Jhuman rushed up to him. They found that the way had been opened and they could go out.

Under the heap of black coal lay Poltu who had willingly courted death that they might live.

ASOKE VIJAY RAHA

The Magic Tree

There was once a tree.
As soon as it was evening
It lifted up its arms and engaged in a ghostly dance.
Again at other times,
When sudden clouds gathered over the forest
And shot out lightning flashes,
The tree puffed its shoulders and grumbled like a bear:
But when it started to rain it shivered as with fever.

When after a sharp shower
The rain stopped and the moon smiled
There would be no trace of either the bear or the tree,
But only a crown studded with a million diamond fish.
I could never understand what happened
In the half light and half shadow of early dawn.
But when the morning was bright
I found that not a fish was left—
I only saw that there was a silver curtain of glistening light.

ANNADA SANKAR RAY

Wealth and Women

I

THE doctor asked, "Will you lend me some books on modern philosophy if you have any? Where can I find some in this country town? To whom can I go?" He appeared to be deeply concerned.

"So you want to unravel the mysteries of the universe?" I said, teasing him, thinking that the doctor had suddenly developed a desire to turn philosopher.

"Oh, no, no! I keep away from that sort of thing. I eat, sleep and make merry. Some day I'll argue about it with you."

"Then what will you do with the books?"

"They are not for me. An interesting case has come to the hospital. It's not the case that is interesting but the patient. He is famous and learned and a forest hermit. You may have heard of him."

I was intrigued and asked the name.

"Dr. Barodekar. That was his former name. Now he is Swami Anandatirtha."

"Which Barodekar? The one who was at Oxford?"

"The same. You know all about him, I see."

I knew little more than his name. I felt a desire to know when he had turned a sanyasi and why. "What is the matter with him?" I asked, "How did he come here?"

"Sciatica. Come along with me to see him some day. If you like I can take you today. I'm on my way to the hospital now."

I was interested but there was no time. I promised to go another day. Taking out a couple of books I gave them to the doctor. The books were modern but not on philosophy. The doctor took them. "Thanks," he said, "You've helped me out of one difficulty but—"

He hesitated. I pressed him to go on. "This will satisfy one of his cravings. I wonder what I'll do about the other."

Observing my curiosity he smiled, "I don't dare to disclose it to you. Our hospital will lose all its reputation. But what can I do? Rules don't apply to sadhus and sanyasis."

Bringing his mouth close to my ear he whispered, "Ganja."

I laughed aloud and asked, "What next !"

"Where am I to find it for him every day?" he grew thoughtful again.

"Why? Are there no other sadhus or sanyasis in the town?"

"Huh," without raising his voice again the doctor got into his car.

How shocking it was ! I thought. A celebrated Oxford intellectual turning forest hermit ! A man who read the latest books on philosophy addicted to ganja ! Well, here he had turned up in a small undistinguished town near the border of Bengal ! I felt impelled to go and see him. I wanted to hear the story of his adventures.

One day I sent a note to the doctor first and then presented myself at the hospital. The sanyasi was confined to bed in one corner of the general ward. No better arrangements could be made for a patient who could not pay. But even though he was a free patient everyone was all attention to him. If he felt the slightest inconvenience, someone came running at once.

In reply to my questions about his health he said, "I'm very well, thank you. They look after me like a king."

The doctor modestly protested, "If we could, we would look after you like an emperor. You will have to put up with some discomfort for several more days."

"I left home in order to be uncomfortable," he joked, "unless you allow me to enjoy my aches and pains it will all have been in vain."

I was told he had contracted this illness through his own fault. He had walked to Puri all the way from Hardwar to see the god Jagannath. He lived in a cave to the north of Hardwar with some fellow-sanyasis. The Maharaja of Tehri has provided the caves with electric light. Such a blending of ancient and modern is rare elsewhere. The sanyasis are well supplied with books and magazines, English, Sanskrit and Hindi. It is an ideal place for tapasya (penance). Now and then the sadhus went out on pilgrimage, travelling on foot as far as was practicable.

Our sanyasi had obtained permission to come as far as Banaras. There he took it into his head to visit Gaya and walked the additional distance. From Gaya he might have gone back but instead he went to the Car Festival at Puri. Again he walked. This affliction was the result of excessive confidence in his physical powers. The hospital authorities at Puri did not allow him to remain in their care for very long. After brief stays of two or three days at other hospitals, he had at length got as far as our place. The authorities here also were not willing to let him stay indefinitely. He was planning to move on to another hospital in Bihar when he managed to get the railway fare. It was impossible for him to walk. He intended to return to Hardwar by train. From there he would go back to his cave.

"There is no experience," he said, "from which some benefit cannot be derived. It is good for me to have lost the use of my legs and to be lying about like an inanimate object. This has brought a sympathetic person like you to see me. You sent me books which I have enjoyed reading. This is the first of Schweitzer's books I have read. I've wanted to read them for a long time."

After a chat about Schweitzer I took my leave. "The day you go away," I said, "you must come to dine with me. We can have a long talk. I hope you will get well soon."

I had several more of Schweitzer's books, so I sent them over.

II

A B O U T a month later he came to my house in a rickshaw. He had to be helped down and up the steps into the sitting room. The floor of the sitting room was slippery and a guest had once fallen on it. I had to warn him to be careful.

The peculiar advantage of the house was an open veranda on all four sides. The veranda was broad and spacious and not slippery. I explained this to the swami and he at once agreed to our moving there. We seated ourselves comfortably in a couple of easy chairs. It was late in the evening.

"Pardon me," I said, "I shall not address you as Swamiji but as Dr. Barodekar. I cannot reconcile myself to this finale for an intellectual of your attainments."

"All that is like something which took place in some other life," he smiled amiably, "I don't care to think about it even though it does come to mind at times."

As we talked philosophy I now and then touched upon his former life. Every time he countered with, "Sadhus are forbidden to speak of those things."

Fruit and milk and puffed rice with a few sweetmeats were ready for him. A small table was drawn up and his meal served where he sat. I asked, "Are you also forbidden to meet women?"

"No, why should we be? We are modern sanyasis."

Then my wife came in, bringing his food on a tray herself.

"I have often been a guest in people's houses," he remarked as he ate, "and I have found householders more truly religious than ascetics. They excel not only in piety but in spiritual elevation also."

"How is that possible?" I asked in surprise, "Householders are under the spell of women and wealth; they are not free."

"My experience is otherwise," he went on slowly. "Men who live in caves are not always worthy of the high opinion which outsiders have of them. They do not have correct values. Those who take pride in having forsworn women and wealth consider those two very things to be of the greatest value."

We were listening. "People who crave food twice a day, who feel badly unless they get their fill to eat, are slaves also. But they are not tied down to one place and are able to go anywhere they like. That is the difference."

"Is it a negligible difference?"

"Not negligible certainly but neither very extraordinary. The two things which are a curse to a householder are no less a source of trouble to ascetics. No one can live on air. Without at least one meal a day no spiritual progress is possible. About the other thing it is better not to speak."

My wife got up and left. "Then," I asked, "what is changed when one becomes a sanyasi? And what is the harm if one returns to the world?"

"There is no going back. Neither do I want to. But I am not so presumptuous as to imagine that I am a free person just because I have become a sanyasi. No one should be."

After his dinner I noticed that he was restless. "Would you like some betel-nut?" I asked.

"No, thank you."

"Cigarettes?"

"No, thanks."

A little later a medical student came and asked to see him. "I need to be alone now for a while," the swami said, "please ask the student to come in."

I went away. The student entered and handed him something. He gave it all his attention. From the smell I understood what it was; it was a familiar odour. I had been ex-officio chairman of the Ganja Society. Perhaps by Ganja Society you have understood a club of drug addicts. It was not that. It was a cooperative society of hemp growers which was controlled by the government because hemp is an excise crop.

The smoke slowly filled the house. My wife was exasperated. "An Oxford graduate!" she exclaimed, "With such a weakness!"

"When he was a don at Oxford," I said, "he was a don. Now

he is a cave-dwelling ascetic. When one goes to Rome one does as the Romans do."

She did not agree with me. Then I had to disclose to her the fact that ascetics frequently turned to the drug, a third curse, in order to escape from the second curse of which the swami had spoken. It is pardonable.

III

S O M E time later the swami sent for me. I found him very listless. He had finished his smoke. The pipe had been taken away.

I sat down in my chair without comment.

"Perhaps it shocks you to see Dr. Barodekar in such a state," he said of his own accord, "If his life had turned out otherwise he would have been shocked himself. There was a time when I used to make fun of sadhus and sanyasis. I didn't know that my fate was to become one of them. Destiny is tricky."

The drug was acting. He had forgotten that sadhus are forbidden to speak of such things.

"Have you ever been to Oxford?"

"Yes."

"My college was Christ Church. How happy I was while I was there! I went after the war. My family was wealthy and I did not have to worry about money. It is a mistake to go to Oxford unless you have means. For the first few years I gave parties and attended parties, going all out on the social front. But I never forgot myself. I thought. There is nothing to compare with the pleasure of thinking. At night I studied. The pleasure that I derived from books was also imcomparable. I wanted to compete with the best and be pre-eminent. And I did excel."

I was listening quietly and did not interrupt him.

"My guardians wanted me to enter the Indian Civil Service. But I did not want to leave Oxford so soon. I deliberately did badly in the Service entrance examination. My guardians were surprised and annoyed. They ordered me to study for the Bar. I failed in that also."

"But I have never heard of anyone failing!"

"Yes, I had a hard time doing it. I found it difficult. In answer to the questions on Roman Law I had to write metaphysics."

I could not help laughing. He went on in the same toneless way, "I came back to my country with a doctorate but I refused the offer of a government job. The Non-Cooperation Movement was in progress at the time. The temper of the country had changed. Gandhi was in jail. I took a post in a private college on a small salary. My guardians were furious. I had not realised until then that the vast sums of money spent on me were an investment. My guardians hammered the fact into me. My mother was commissioned to select a wealthy wife for me in order that the loss might be made good— in one way if not in another....

"My ambition," he hesitated for a moment, "was to be the greatest philosopher in India. I had no objection to marriage if I found a girl who would be of help to me in my work. There was a certain girl student in London, an Indian girl. She might have made a fit wife for me if we had married. But hers was not a highly placed family; they had no money. My guardians objected to setting up ties of kinship with them. The girl was not very good-looking and she was also a little over the most suitable age for marriage. Mother took a dislike to her on these grounds. My well-wishers were alarmed when they heard I wanted to be a philosopher. They began to look for a girl that would tie me down, make me a family man and make me rich. I grew stubborn and refused to marry."

His voice was gradually growing unnatural as the voices of drug addicts do.

"Several years passed. My mother could think of no way to tie me down. She fell ill. Very probably the illness was self-induced. I was informed by wire that she was on her death-bed and wished to see me. I had to dash from Bombay to Baroda. I found everyone wiping their eyes. The doctor had given up hope it seems. When I entered her room Mother called me to her with a gesture. A girl I didn't know was sitting beside her. She took our hands and put them together. Then she cried. My sister had come in behind us. She whispered in my ear, 'If you want Mother to live, say you are willing.' I did not understand what it was to which I had to agree. 'I'm willing,' I said mechanically. Conchs sounded outside. Then I realised that I had agreed to marry. It is impossible to back out once you give your word. Mother got well and I was married."

"After that?" I asked, all attention.

"After that things went as they usually do. The first few months passed in festivity and happiness. The girl was beautiful and refined. She did her best to make me happy. But she was not educated. How could an intellectual derive pleasure from talking to her? It was futile to try to make her understand who and what I was or what my work was. We inhabited two different worlds. We lived together but neither really knew the other. On the whole, our days did not pass unpleasantly. We were a more or less happy couple. But what I earned was not enough. And I felt an aversion for touching my wife's property. So when a Maharaja offered me the post of tutor to his sons, I accepted it. We did not have to leave Bombay. The Maharaja had a palace there. The princes stayed in Bombay in order to pursue their studies. Of course their studies were studies only in name. They kept themselves busy with sports and the pleasures of society. I found ample time for my own work. But my wife, coming under the influence of the princely household, developed into a society woman. How could I use my leisure to study philosophy? I had to look after the children! I could not turn them over to the care of the servants without worrying about them. And our expenses rose from day to day. If I complained to her she would answer, 'I am living on my own money, not on yours.'

To which I would reply, 'What was the need to marry me in order to do that?' 'Why do women marry?' she retorted. No answer to that has ever occurred to me. Can you tell me why women marry?''

I was put out and said, "Oh, just—"

"Uh. You can't get out of it like that. The more you think about it the more you'll sweat over it. Many thinkers have given it careful thought. None of them has ever arrived at a settled conclusion. Frustrated, they have slandered women. They are to blame for being desirable! As if men aren't! Wealth has been tagged on to them, as though it were equally divine! My vanity was hurt even though my wife was not spending my money. When I raised any objection she would answer, 'You spent your father's money freely enough when you were at Oxford. Assume that my father, instead of sending me to Oxford, gave me away in marriage. What am I doing that you have not done? What is wrong with it?' What she said could not just be brushed aside. I also had mixed in Society in my time. She was doing what I had done at her age. Yet I did not like it in the least. It seemed to me that there must be an answer even though I could not think of one. Our old-fashioned elders would have stood no nonsense. As the Sans-krit saying has it, 'No woman deserves to be free.' We moderns can't say that. We write theses. Dissatisfaction was growing in my heart because my philosophical thinking had been deflec-ted into wrong channels.''

IV

H I S voice, growing progressively more and more hoarse, was now indistinct. "Would you like a drink of water?" I asked.

"No water, but some milk or cocoa, if I may," he answered.

I sent for a cup of cocoa.

"There was talk of the young princes being sent to Oxford. The Maharaja wanted me to accompany them. I also wanted

to go to Oxford again and re-establish contacts with philosophers there. What were they thinking? What were they
writing? I felt the desire to know. To tour the Continent from
there was an old dream of mine. But it was painful to leave
my wife and children behind. I had not the means to take
them with me. I would have had to use my wife's money. My
heart refused to do that...."

The cocoa came. He continued slowly, "There was a quarrel
with my wife over it. I sent her to her father's. I explained
that I was going to England because I had work to do, not for
pleasure. If she had had work to do she would have gone too.
But she didn't even look after the house or take care of the
children. I had to do everything. My work was being ruined.
She replied harshly that, in that case, it was useless for me to
go. 'I don't believe that you'll live like a monk while you are
there. Why should you make me suffer?' she cried. The more
I tried to explain the wilder she became. But what could I do?
There was no way for me to take my family abroad with me.
I went alone. It was as I had apprehended. Philosophy had
progressed a long way in my absence. And I had dropped
behind to that extent. I would have to work very hard. Month
after month passed trying to catch up with those who had got
ahead of me. How can women understand a thing like that?
She could only write letters begging me to come back. 'Come
back, our son is running a temperature,' 'Come back, our
daughter had an attack of dysentery, come back, she is
losing her mind.' Holtby was of my year. The reputation he
had made for himself in this short time was astonishing. He
was like Haldane and I was like P. K. Ray. He regarded me
with pity. How can a woman understand what that means
to a man! I wrote a thesis. Holtby glanced through it and
said, 'You're a Rip Van Winkle! All these theories were
discarded long ago.' "

Barodekar sighed deeply and said, "My life has been wasted!
It's been of no use to anybody. Holtby was a poor boy. He
did not marry. He had clung to Oxford in order to gain know-

ledge and add something of his own to the existing stock.
And I! Obedient to my father I had gone home, obedient to
my mother I had married, for the sake of my wife I had become a tutor in a princely household! Holtby would some day
be the equal of Alexander or of Bertrand Russell while I—I
would be reduced to writing textbooks! The very idea of that
took all the flavour out of my life. When a telegram came from
home saying that my son had typhoid and I was to return
immediately by air if I wished to see him, I did not believe it.
It appeared to me to be a staged affair as my mother's illness
had been staged. They were determined not to allow me to
become a famous philosopher. They would drag me back to
India and say a chair had fallen vacant at some university
and insist on my trying for it. I refused to put my foot into
the trap. I would stay at Oxford as long as I possibly could.
I enquired after the boy by long distance telephone. I was
upset by what I heard. I forced myself to remember that
Karl Marx had not been deflected from his work although he
too lost a son. Was there any certainty that the boy would
recover if I went back to India? If I once went, would I ever
get away again? No, I refused to go."

The sanyasi's eyes were wet. "He died," he said thickly.
"Up to the end he believed that his father would come to him,
flying over the clouds. He lay under the open sky and stared
up into it, asking now and then, 'Where is he? Where is
Daddy?' His last words were, 'Daddy, Daddy.' The grief I
felt when I heard the news is something I shall never be able
to make anybody understand! To it was added a sense of guilt.
It seemed to me that I was the one who ought to have died.
Of what use was my life to anybody! If the boy had lived he
would have been able to give so much to the world. I found
no consolation and no peace in philosophy. Thought is powerless in such matters. The mind is defeated. I felt a revulsion
towards the whole subject of philosophy. It seemed childish
to me to study philosophy in order to make a name for myself.
In the light of my personal crisis I came to know myself. I

did not want knowledge for its own sake as Holtby did. I was
ambitious. But at what price?"

This time he asked for water. Water was brought. His
throat was dry.

"I resigned from my post as tutor to the princes and went
home. I found that my wife had been removed to a mental
hospital. I held out my arms to my daughter but my mother-
in-law came between us. 'We have nothing more to do with
you,' she said, 'you are no more to us than any passer-by in
the street. This child does not go to strangers.' My daughter
had been so alienated from me that she did not even call me
Daddy. She turned away from me. Yet that girl was the light
of my eyes. I had walked up and down with her in my arms
days and nights together. She used to cry at night. I used to
get up and go to her bedside, caress her until she was quiet.
Her mother did not get up. She did not waken easily. When
she did wake up she would ask me to go to the child. It is
doubtful whether the girl even recognised me. Driven to despair by my daughter's indifference I left home like King Lear.
I wandered from place to place and met many sadhus. Then
on a certain day I found my guru. He advised me not to give
up the world but to take care of my wife and look after my
daughter. Acting on his suggestion I tried it for a time. Vain
effort ! How can one who is not mad be cured of madness?
Such things are too intimate to be spoken of, even to one's
guru. He understood by implication. Then he gave me my
initiation, my *mantra*. That was eleven years ago. No news of
his family is sent to one who has left the world. I have refrained from making enquiries and they have refrained from com-
municating with me. I do not even know whether my wife
is alive or not. If she is, where she is, at her father's or in a
mental home? My parents died long ago. Our girl is old enough
to be married now. She will be eighteen this fall. The age for
marriage is slowly rising in our country. I hope she will stay
unmarried as long as she can. It hurts me to think that she
might fall into the hands of an unworthy husband like me.

No, it is better for her not to marry at all."

After this he began to babble nonsense, delirious with the drug. I had not the heart to disturb him. It had grown late. His train left at midnight. If he could get a little sleep before then it would do him good.

The doctor's voice was heard outside. He had come with his car to take the swami to the station. A bed would be spread for him in the station waiting room. He could rest there. A ticket to Dhanbad had been purchased for him in advance. The Dhanbad hospital had agreed to admit him.

We helped him into the car. When he was seated he exclaimed, "My pipe? Who has my pipe?" Someone had to dash back to the verandah for the pipe. He took hold of it as if he were taking hold of heaven and put it into the pocket of his robe with tender care. Then, looking at me, the famous and learned Dr. Barodekar exclaimed, 'Vyom! Vyom! Babu Sahib, Vyom! Vyom!"

The car moved away.

PRABODH KUMAR SANYAL

A Virtuous Woman

A FEW birds with coloured plumes were already in
evidence in the Bhimpedi Valley. The winter was almost
over. We were on our way to the shrine of Pashupatinath in
Nepal to see the god on his day of advent in early spring.

We passed the stages of Rexaul and Amlakgunj without
much difficulty. We had not faced any real hardship but
how could one expect the comforts of city life on such a journey? After we left Bhimpedi, we had to cross high mountains
on foot. When at last we reached the inn at Kulekhani, it was
late and we were famished.

Our group was made up of the genuine stuff of India. You
see them on the way to shrines everywhere: ascetics, beggars,
cripples, men in disguise, women of low caste and many of
them old. Without careful scrutiny it was difficult to say who
came from where. Two of us were from Bengal but were completely assimilated in the miscellaneous crowd. In dress and
conduct, in dirtiness and filth, we were all just the same.
One reason for this was that any suggestion of affluence would
attract beggars and possibly thieves and lead to the loss of
our few possessions. I had learnt this in the course of many
pilgrimages in different parts of India, but I was not the
only one to know that not all pilgrims in our party had joined
us for the pilgrimage alone!

The river starts as a thin stream but gradually swells as
other streams join it. Between Kulekhani and Chetlang, our
party also grew. We were all travellers on foot. There were
neither animals to ride nor vehicles of any type. Of course
when the nobility travelled, they made their own arrangements.

257

They were carried, but the only vehicle was a *jhapan*, a kind of chair carried on men's shoulders.

We were travelling through bare and rock-studded valleys. There were no signs of human habitation anywhere. We did not know what awaited us but, since we were moving to the capital city, we felt sure that some shelter would be found. It was as if we were crossing the vast legendary steppes in hope and fear.

Before we reached Chetlang, we had already become a large party. It was difficult to spot out any individual but together we constituted a band. Men and women, lame and blind and invalid, each member was different, and yet everyone had the stamp of a common purpose. We could see the crowd but no individuals. My experience had taught me that nothing is so oppressive, meaningless and boring as an amorphous crowd.

When we reached Chetlang, we saw the rest house for pilgrims built by the king. We saw the rest house but could find no room in it. Disappointed, we sought shelter on the banks of the river. It was the end of the winter high up in the hills. As we approached the river, the swift current seemed to give edge to the cold winds. The day was moving fast towards evening. Our tired bodies were hungering for food and rest. Our first aim was to find some shelter which would protect us from the biting wind and give an opportunity to look for food. When at last we found a small tent, we entered it and slumped down on the damp cold grass with our blankets pulled right up to our ears. A few pilgrims were already there and had occupied the few mats which were spread on the ground. Our legs felt numb and cold as we put down our baggage and sat in a corner, grateful for this shelter against the wind.

I was thinking how to boil a little rice and pulses to assuage my hunger, when another band of pilgrims invaded our tent. There was hardly room for us and we protested angrily against their entry. Some three or four men and women moved away but two of them refused to budge. They begged of us to let them stay in a corner, for they had nowhere else to go. We had been shivering in the cold in the impending gloom of the winter evening and had hardly noticed the newcomers, but now I saw that one of them was a woman.

She had somehow managed to find a few square feet and had spread her blanket. She was from Upper India and was wearing a sari with a black border and a quilted cotton coat. She could not be more than thirty or so but what struck me was the sudden change in her mien. Even five minutes ago, she was an humble supplicant begging for shelter. Now that she had found a berth, her whole attitude changed. The hardly suppressed pride in her youth and beauty seemed already to warm the cold atmosphere inside the tent. She let down her hair and started combing it with a wooden comb. For the last two or three days we had been lost in a jostling crowd of nameless humanity. Today this woman suddenly stood out from the crowd and proudly proclaimed her individuality.

It is true we had given her shelter but now her self-posession and tidiness made us feel ashamed. Her very presence seemed to dominate all inside the tent.

I got up, went out and started to prepare some food. As I was about to re-enter, an old sanyasi of gigantic proportions appeared on the scene. As soon as she saw him, the woman cried out in a sharp tone, "Look at this scoundrel of a sanyasi who has been pursuing me all these days."

None of us was prepared for this sudden development. We were shocked by the woman's cry and looked at the sanyasi. Clothed in saffron robes, the giant towered over all of us. He was quite bald in front but ringlets of white hair hung from the back of his head. I asked the woman, "What is the matter?"

The woman said, "This old scoundrel has been following me since yesterday. Wherever I go, he appears. He tries to flirt with me and hold my hands."

She turned to the sanyasi and said, "Get out from here. I will not stand all this nonsense. Do you understand? Get out."

I looked at the sanyasi. His face was unruffled. There was a gentle smile on it. It seemed that he was full of an unbounded affection for the entire womanhood of the world.

The woman turned round and faced in the opposite direction. Not only so, she wrapped herself up in her blanket as if to hide her body from his hungry eyes.

Like a python which moves slowly and silently but inexorably, the old sanyasi came into the tent with slow, silent steps. We were all furious at him. I asked him, "What is your intention?"

The sanyasi smiled and said, "Nothing."

"There is no room inside. Why are you then coming in?"

The sanyasi gave no reply but moved another step forward and looked around to find a vacant spot. We were packed like sardines. Without using physical force, it would be impossible for anyone to make room for himself. Besides, the way he had been pursuing this unwilling woman had evoked disgust and hatred among all the men in the tent. None of us were willing to make room for him. But his appearance was terrifying. His long white beard covered his chest. His two long arms were strong and hairy. His eyes were brown like those of a tiger. All told, he looked like a descendant—perhaps the last descendant—of the giants. We were worried but did not know how to prevent him coming in.

My companion said, "You better clear out from here. There is no room for you. If you make trouble, I shall call the king's soldiers."

It was for us an unknown area. Perhaps there were sentries and soldiers to protect the pilgrims. Who, however, was going to look for them through this crowd and on this cold winter night? We were all tired and hungry. No one had the spirit or the energy. The old sanyasi was fully conscious of this fact. He knew as well as we that our verbal protests were futile.

He took two steps more inside the tent. In helpless anger, we glared at him. If looks could scorch, he would have certainly burnt. The scriptures say that Kamadeva was turned to ashes when Siva looked at him in anger but our eyes lacked the electric fire which Siva had. Suddenly, we thought: Why need we worry? When we started for the shrine, we had left all social conventions behind us. Pashupatinath himself would look after the honour of this pilgrim woman. We certainly had no responsibility for her.

The woman had a free and easy manner. Her looks and her movements were unembarrassed. She had come on her own and surely she could look after herself. What else could we then do but keep quiet? The tent belonged to everybody.

The persistent sanyasi made room for himself close to us. Our protests, our resistance and our disgust were equally without avail. The woman allowed the sanyasi to sit next to her more or less as a man, in reluctant disgust, allows a dog to sit next to him on a winter night. She however tried to raise a wall between them with her bundles and her utensils. Sharply she said: "I warn you not to try to steal my things, you robber."

The sanyasi kept on smiling. The woman turned in disgust and started preparing betel-leaf for herself.

It was cold and damp outside but we put together a few stones and cooked a little rice and pulses with the damp fuel. We had hidden in our stores some forbidden food. We were therefore glad of the darkness that enabled us to take it without the others' knowledge. We figured out that, after we left Chetlang, we would reach the capital of Nepal some time next afternoon.

We had spent almost two hours outside and were numb and cold, but the food had been warm and we were satisfied because of the forbidden food we had taken. We were now even ready to apply physical force in order to save a woman's honour. I shaped a branch of a tree into a heavy staff and carried it into the tent with me. I felt confident that Pashupatinath wanted us to look after the honour of this pilgrim woman.

We received the shock of our lives when we came inside.

The woman was sitting in her own area but she had lighted a candle and was chewing betel-leaf. The sanyasi was reading the scriptures to her in the light of her candle. The bundles still divided their beds but on the two sides the two beds were arranged carefully. All the other pilgrims inside the tent were full of reverence for the old sanyasi.

How many people can boast of such an experience? Outside, the night was dark. The roads to the mountain shrine were unknown to us. By the tent flowed the Bagmati and we could hear her incessant gurgle as she flowed over her stony bed. Now and then wild animals howled fearfully. Inside, we were a handful of pilgrims who had left the known world behind. In the centre sat a young woman and near her hovered this sanyasi reading the scriptures. As soon as we came in, the woman offered us betel-leaf. The sanyasi also opened his bundle and smiled at us as he offered us a few fruits and sweets. We accepted the gifts with bowed heads.

I hid the staff I had made, for it was no longer necessary. I thought that both the scenes I had seen were equally true. I had heard that on these pilgrim journeys men often develop unusual passions. Equally often, they are swept away by a deep feeling of reverence. They were two manifestations of the same power. There was a luminous glow on the sanyasi's face. The woman's face also looked soft and mellow, it was no longer intense and bitter. Unless you have felt the sense of being alone among a vast crowd of pilgrims, you could not understand what had happened.

Somehow the talk turned to the woman's home life. She came from the U.P. She was a Kurmi and her name was Ram Pyari. Her husband had turned her out because she was barren. He had threatened to marry again. Ram Pyari was therefore going to the shrine of Pashupatinath. Either she would have a child or she would put an end to her life. Her husband, she said, was god-like. We were all deeply impressed by her devotion to her husband.

The discussion on the scriptures continued long. One after

another the pilgrims dropped off to sleep. We do not know when we also pulled up our blankets and left Ram Pyari in the protection of Pashupatinath. The candle burnt on as with restless energy the old sanyasi went on explaining the scriptures to the beautiful young woman.

Those who have gone on a pilgrimage know how difficult it is to wake pilgrims once they fall asleep. There are however rows which are too much for even the tired pilgrims. It is difficult to say how late in the night it was. But suddenly a terrible uproar and the sound of a struggle shook us from our slumber. We had forgotten that we were pilgrims on a difficult mountain way. We hardly remembered that we were inside a tent by the side of a river near the snow-line. It therefore took us a little time to collect our wits and to realise where we were in this darkness. Then I suddenly remembered the staff I had made but, when I searched for it, I found it had disappeared. Later I came to know that the old sanyasi had removed it from my side.

As we rubbed our eyes and sat up, we heard Ram Pyari's sharp and angry voice.

She was abusing the sanyasi, "Don't you realise I am a virtuous woman, you scoundrel? You pretend to be a sanyasi and behave like this. Don't you know that I am a chaste wife?"

We heard the sound of sharp blows. We realised that Ram Pyari had taken her slipper off and was using it on the bald head of the old sanyasi.

Now that we were up, the woman addressed us, "I appeal to all of you. I have already told him that I am a good woman. I am not what he thinks. I have my husband. I have a home and I must go back as chaste as I came. This scoundrel of a sanyasi tried to put his hands on me with evil intentions."

The sanyasi listened to all this abuse silently and with bowed head. Whether there was still a luminous glow in his eyes, we could not see in the dark but he remained still and dumb like a stone.

Ram Pyari's voice again rang out sharply, "You pressed my hands, I said nothing. You touched my face, even then I did not complain. But how can I, a virtuous woman, allow you to paw me? I shall kick you, you son of a bitch."

Outside, the night was bitterly cold. No one was in a mood to fight or complain. The sentry and the soldiers of the king had all disappeared. I was helpless without my staff. Besides it seemed absurd for us to try to beat this giant of a man.

I suggested that Ram Pyari should change places with us. We would sleep next to the sanyasi and Ram Pyari could occupy the place where we were. We could then sleep for at least two more hours. If she remained out of the reach of the sanyasi, her honour would surely be safe.

The objection came from Ram Pyari. She was an independent woman of Upper India, not a helpless Bengali girl, she said. She raised her eyebrows and protested. "Why should I move from my place? This spot is mine and I stay here. Besides, I am a woman of virtue and am not afraid of a robber like this fellow. I will not move."

Her statement was of course true. A virtuous woman fears nothing. The scriptures say that she can defy even death. It is only worthless creatures like us who have no faith in the power and dignity of a virtuous woman. Ram Pyari had really shamed all of us. A woman of virtue fears neither wild animals, nor robbers nor even death. This fellow was after all only a sanyasi. We drew up our blankets and again lay down to sleep.

Ram Pyari was now quieter. She no longer shouted but she went on giving sound advice to the old ruffian, "You must mend your ways and never pursue an unwilling woman. I am the daughter of a respectable family. I am married and, so long as my husband is alive, I cannot think of another man. I am not the type of woman you are after. I am again lying down. You are a sanyasi and you are old. You should never worry me again. However, I am sorry I had to beat you because of your wickedness."

She had lighted the candle again. She took another betel-leaf and carefully arranged her hair and lay down. The old sanyasi kept on looking at her through half-closed eyes. His gaze was quiet and restrained, but still it seemed to be full of a strange activity. After some time Ram Pyari put off the light again.

E A R L Y in the dawn we all got up. I found that almost all the pilgrims in the tent had disappeared. There was no trace of either Ram Pyari or the sanyasi. We did not even know whether they had gone together or separately. Nor was it any concern of ours. In any case, we were glad to be rid of them.

From Chetlang we started again on the ancient way. It was a long journey. We had to cross the river and then climb a high hill as steep as a wall. Towards the afternoon, we descended the hill which was slippery and covered with dense forests. In the distance we saw Khatmandu like a dream city. Still farther away, the snow ranges stretched from horizon to horizon. In the centre, the capital of Nepal shone like a point of light.

Most people stay for a week in Khatmandu and we did the same. On the return journey, I fell ill and had to be carried back. The road was the same from Bhimpedi. We went by bus to Amlakgunj and then we took the train to Rexaul.

The labour of these days and specially my illness had made me forget all the incidents of the journey. In fact, I had forgotten all about Ram Pyari but as I was about to get into the train at Amlakgunj, I suddenly saw her. She was hurrying through the crowd, and her gait seemed to arouse waves of passion all around. She was today dressed in a dark sari. Her flesh was firm and tight and there was a strange smile on her face. She did not have to press her way through the crowd. The crowd itself made way for her.

When she got into the train and saw us, she smiled in recognition and said that Pashupatinath had blessed her.

"That is fine. Are you not returning home now?"

In a voice choked with emotion, Ram Pyari said, "Yes, of course. He has granted my prayer; I will have a son."

I reassured her, "Certainly you will have a son. Pashupatinath has blessed you."

Suddenly to our surprise, the old giant of a sanyasi walked into the train. He opened his bag and offered us sweets. He then took Ram Pyari's hand in his and said in a commanding voice, "Let us go and sit there."

Ram Pyari stood up without a word like a devoted wife. Smilingly she said, "So you see, the sanyasi has not left me. He will stay with me for seven days and teach me the scriptures. What am I to do?"

They moved away and sat in a corner all by themselves. The train was about to start. I prayed silently to Pashupatinath, "Let this virtuous woman have her wish fulfilled."

ARUN KUMAR SARKAR

Juhu

Let go the rudder;
The quarry will always elude you;
Come and rest here.
Deceitful day flies fast like fleet-footed golden deer.
Night alone knows
The tears left in the darkness.

Now the glittering sunlight shines
Like handfuls of golden joy lit by the light of the sea.
Let the grasp of greed cease.
Let the night of the disturbed dreams end.
Come and rest here.

The Malabar Hill trembles.
The Arabian Sea is a violent lover
Who will take no denial.
The sea birds shine like blue clouds.
The fearless waves sing in the sunlight.

This turmoil is the essence of the real:
Stable and unstable,
In time and beyond.
My heart that seeks to flee far away
Realises that eternal life is to be found
Inside limitations.

Put on the glistening sunlight like bright colour.
Endless sunlit joy is the song of the sea.
Let go the rudder.
The quarry will always elude you.
Come and rest here.

S U N I L   S A R K A R

Earthworm

The earthworm wanted to know the earth.
In canals and fields, in holes and clefts
It sought to know the utmost reaches of the earth.
The earthworm wanted to know the earth.

Rocky soil, sand or clay or mixed—
It pushed against and felt clods and clumps.
It entered into many tunnels
To bring above the news of lower regions.

It thirsted in the dry dust
And sought relief in the heart of mother earth.
When there was rain and water
It dragged its body joyously through the mud.

Neither in mud nor in slush
Neither by crawling nor rolling
Did it find the secret of the earth.
It then sought the answer in its body's sap.

At last the earthworm died.
It died ignorant of the drama of the earth.
Now that it has become one with the dust
Maybe it seeks a judgement from mother earth herself!

ACHINTYA KUMAR SEN GUPTA

The Bamboo Trick

T H E annual Gajan fair was being held in the maidan at
Khorogachi.

This year the fair wasn't much of a success, it hadn't drawn
the usual crowds, and the variety of things offered for sale
was poor: evil-smelling papadams fried in rancid oil, popcorn
and some hail-ridden green mangoes. The scarcity of paper
had banished the kites and the fluttering paper toys. Clay toys
were there—dogs and cats, horses and elephants—all in one
colour, with only a dot or a line in black to denote an eye or
the end of a tail. Then split-cane and bamboo baskets, fish-
traps etc.—small and large. Earthenware pots and pans, cups
and plates. But the piles of handwoven towels in gay checks
and the glitter of multi-coloured glass bangles were missing.

Those who had come to the fair looked worn-out and lifeless,
as if they had emerged more dead than alive from the bowels
of some dark valley of fear. There was no gaiety either in their
talk or in their walk. The clothes they wore were drab and
shabby—on the verge of turning into rags.

The crowd was thickest under the pakur tree and all the
noise and tumult of the fair had concentrated there.

As I went forward, I heard a child wailing, "I'll fall, I'll die!"
Eyes blind with streaming tears he sobbed and wailed miser-
ably. A little boy, six or seven years old, with arms and legs
like brittle sticks, a strip of rag tied tightly below his waist,
he looked as helpless as a fledgeling fallen from its nest.

"What is it? Why is he crying?"

A bamboo trick was about to be performed, they informed me.

I didn't understand at first. Were they going to beat up the boy with a bamboo and was that why he sobbed so ceaselessly?

No, the bamboo wasn't going to be used for beating him, they explained. It was to be used for a trick—a trick we were shortly to see.

I knew that orders of attachment decreed by a court were sometimes executed by posting a notice on a bamboo pole near the property to be attached, with a beat of drums. But I was not aware of any other trick that could be performed with a piece of bamboo.

Someone asked, "Will the bamboo be planted in the ground?"

"Oh, no, this isn't an ordinary trick of that sort." Someone in the know explained in a tone of authority, "No, the old man will set it on his own tummy and the boy will climb the bamboo-pole and go right up to the top. Then the boy will balance himself on the other end and lie on it face downwards. The bamboo-pole will then start spinning, and the boy with his hands and legs hanging free will spin on top. I've seen them perform many times before."

"Is that the old man?"

"Yes, that's Mantaj."

The old man's body was shrivelled like a piece of twisted rope, a few grey hairs jutted out from his chin. His chest was arched, mound-like, his stomach a concave hollow, and the little flesh he had hung loose from his bones. His deep-set eyes glittered in the afternoon sunshine. It was his eyes alone that gave evidence of whatever courage and skill he had.

The audience fanned out in a circle. Mantaj went round with an empty old tin mug hoping to collect a few coppers.

Someone scolded him: "The show isn't on yet and here you're asking for money!"

But how was the show to commence? The performer who was to do the act of climbing the pole was busy creating a rumpus with his wailing—"I'll fall, I'll die!"

"What is all this wailing for? If you are so jittery about

falling, why come to perform?"

But Mantaj took no notice of the boy's howling. He went round with his tin mug assuring everyone that the show would certainly take place.

"This isn't their first performance, is it? Then why is the boy crying?" I asked the man standing next to me.

"He didn't perform before, he is a novice."

"Then who did it?"

"His elder brother—"

"No, no, this boy too has performed once or twice," someone else protested, "this boy climbed the bamboo when they gave a show during the Saraswati Puja, in the school yard at Tentul. He isn't used to it yet, that day his performance consisted of just climbing up the bamboo. His elder brother is the real performer. But whatever you may say, I feel that the real credit for the trick goes to the man who spins the bamboo— Mantaj."

"Where's his brother?"

"I wish I knew!"

Not a solitary tinkle rang in Mantaj's mug. No one was prepared to part with a copper before the show commenced.

Having no other alternative, Mantaj went towards the boy. The boy screamed in fear as if he was facing a blank wall with a wild dog chasing behind him. "No, no, not I! I'll fall, I'll die—"

The father pulled the boy's hand roughly. He raised his hand to hit the boy.

"Pooh, see how frightened he is! Your father has shown this trick with many a grown-up young man on the bamboo, and now, you think he can't manage you—a stripling of a boy!"

A part of the audience now began to scold the boy on behalf of the father.

Mantaj smiled. Long experience lent a keen edge to his smile.

"Supposing you do slip and fall, won't your father be able to catch you in his arms? Come along, now."

The man who was beating the tom-tom plied his sticks harder.

But the boy refused to budge. The sound of his wailing rose above the din of the fair.

So there was to be no bamboo trick! One, then another, began to slip away.

In exasperation Mantaj craned his neck and looked over the circle of the crowd. A little later, another boy came forward walking on weak, unsteady feet, a half-eaten papadam clutched in his hand.

"That's the brother!" some of the audience shouted.

A sickly looking ten-year-old boy with reedy arms and legs, a torn quilt wrapped round his body. All around his lips, on his cheeks and his chin were marks of cuts that had now become sores. A buzzing fly was worrying him as it settled again and again on the tip of his nose. His two big eyes held a blank meaningless look.

He went to his little brother and said, "Don't cry Akku, I'll climb the pole."

Akku quietened down and his tears dried up almost at once.

The crowd drew closer. The beat of the tom-tom became more frenzied.

Mantaj gathered together and tightened the bit of cloth that hung between his waist and knees. He placed the bamboo on his stomach, in the hollow of his navel. He muttered something indistinctly. Perhaps he sent up a prayer to his god. Then he touched the bamboo to his forehead. He now drew it close to his mouth, whispered something to it, then stroked it with his hands.

Nobody had ever seen him behave thus—so lacking in poise, as he was now.

"Come on, Imtaj," he called out to his elder son.

In a moment Imtaj whipped off the torn quilt from his body.

It was as if something had hit me—I gasped in horror. The boy's chest and stomach were covered with sores which ran in long streaks. Scabs had formed on some, others were

raw gaping wounds, some had festered and swelled with pus.
That wretched fly had fetched a number of buzzing blue-
bottles to share his feast.

I felt a little relieved when the boy turned his back to me.
His back was smooth, spotless.

"How did he get those sores? So many sores?" I asked.

Some of them knew, I learnt. On the festival of spring,
while performing at the house of the zamindar at Champali,
Imtaj had slipped. The old man had just recovered from a
bout of malaria and couldn't manage to get even a handful
of cold wet rice while he was convalescing. That was the
reason why he couldn't keep the bamboo balanced on his
stomach. Where Imtaj fell, the ground was covered with gravel
and broken tiles, and it had badly cut and bruised his chest
and stomach. The boy had been out of sorts ever since.

"Won't you wrap yourself with that rag?" asked Mantaj.

"No." The boy rubbed both hands with dust and jumped
up on the bamboo pole which by then rested on his father's
stomach. With the suppleness of long practice, he began
climbing up swiftly. Mantaj stood motionless, still, the bamboo
gripped in both hands and pressed into the pit of his stomach.

"Let him see, let Akkas see, how willingly his brother has
come to perform despite his sores!"

With his face turned upwards, Akkas or Akku stared at his
brother. He had nothing to fear now. He could beat the tom-
tom or go round with the mug if he so wished.

On reaching the top of the bamboo, Imtaj paused for a
moment, then he gathered his cloth together to fix the pole-
end against his stomach. His sores became visible again. The
sight was unbearable. I turned to leave.

Somebody stopped me. He said, "When he lies stuck up
on the pole like a frog, his arms and legs hanging loose, and
starts spinning round and round in space, you won't see those
sores any more!"

"Does the father turn the bamboo with his hands?"

"He turns the bamboo with his hands a few times, then

stuck on his navel, it spins on its own momentum. That's really the trick."

Someone else cut in: "To display acrobatics on a bamboo planted in the ground has become out of date now—what's so clever about that?"

The bamboo in the mean time had started spinning in Mantaj's hand. The boy must have become very light after his fall, he was spinning as fast as a paper cartwheel. His arms and legs were spread out and his hideous sores were no longer visible. One could hardly make out whether it was a human being or bat or flying fox that was whirling in space.

My gaze had been fixed skywards, now I turned my eyes to Mantaj when he suddenly placed the revolving pole in his navel and let go his hands. The father's belly, rather than his son's, was a sight worth seeing. The son's stomach was a mass of sores, but the father's stomach was a great big hollow. This pit was not something contrived for the moment to dig in the bamboo. I felt this deep pit must have been there for a long, long time. And who knows what fiery churnstick was churning away inside that pit?

I could hardly believe my eyes when I saw how far back the bamboo-end had pressed into his stomach. I had seen men with bellies flattened to their backs before this. But now I saw a man who seemed to have no belly at all—the bamboo seemed to press straight into his back from the front. His very entrails had shrivelled and disappeared nobody knew where. At each turn the bamboo clattered against his backbone.

What I was apprehending every moment came about, but it was not Imtaj who slipped, it was Mantaj who reeled and crashed to the ground. At the last moment he had held out his hands to catch the falling boy. But however frail the boy was, his father's arms were not strong enough to support him.

"Nowadays the old man seems to be slipping again and again...." someone complained.

Mantaj squatted on his haunches with his head pressed into his hands, panting like a hard-run old horse. He was staring blankly at his empty mug.

No wonder he had taken round the mug before starting the performance. Had he obtained a few coppers, he could have eaten something—one or two papadams, or perhaps a few of the leathery batter-fried onion and brinjal slices selling nearby. A morsel of food could have made all the difference, it would perhaps have given some strength to his weary old arms. Long habit could train one to bear most things except perhaps to quench the pangs of hunger. The bamboo, the helpless arms, the son, the sores— one could face each in its turn with the courage that practice and experience endows—but hunger—it was unruly, ruthless.

The bamboo had skipped and fallen at a distance, and Imtaj still further away. The din of the crowd drowned his groans. Someone said, "He's finished." Said another: "His heart is still beating!"

There was a charitable hospital nearby. Some people carried Imtaj there, doing their best to avoid contact with his sores. The accident had just happened, the hospital could hardly dare turn away the patient. Had Imtaj gone there to have his sores attended to, they would have driven him away because Mantaj couldn't always pay the one-anna bit they demanded for medicine. If half-an-anna or one anna came his way, was Mantaj to spend it on medicine for sores that covered the stomach or to soothe the sores that burned inside!

Mantaj sat grim and silent, but the younger boy began wailing at the top of his voice. I thought he was crying because of his brother.

But no, it was the same lament, in a still more helpless tone: "It's my turn now! It's my turn! I'm sure to fall, I'll die—"

Without a word Mantaj got up, took Akku by the hand and walked towards the hospital.

"I'll fall, I'll die!" What unseen god was being beseeched by a child's piteous wails—for a misery which knew no remedy.

Mantaj remained silent. His stony face looked cruel in its chill detachment. This hard cold silence was the only reply he could give his son. What else could he do? He must eat.

NOTES ON AUTHORS

BANAPHOOL (b. 1899, Purnea)
Pseudonym of BALAICHAND MUKHOPADHYAY

A medical man by profession. Started as a writer of poems but has achieved distinction through his short stories. Interested in the dramatic incident rather than in reflection or ideals or social consciousness. Has an abundant gift of humour and often achieves striking effects by a series of paradoxes. Pays great attention to technique and often compresses a story into a page or so. Has a real flair for drama, but seems more attracted to the novel and the short story.

Chief works: Dvairath, Kichhukshan, Nirmok, Banaphooler Galpa,
  Banaphooler aro galpa, Banaphooler Kavita, Vidyasagar,
  Sri Madhusudan.

BIBHUTIBHUSAN BANDOPADHYAY (1896-1950, b. Jessore)
Novelist and story writer who achieved immediate fame with his book, *Pather Panchali*. Has used the recollections of childhood and youthful travels with great effect. One of the finest interpreters of rural Bengal. His novels and stories deal with human beings but the dominant character is rural nature. The hardships and difficulties of village people are delineated with great realism, but he also brings out the pathos and beauty of rural life; Bengal's flowers and fields, her folk-lore and traditions as well as the joys and sorrows of the village find vivid expression in his writings. Won the Rabindra Memorial Prize posthumously.

Chief works: Pather Panchali, Aparajita, Aranyak, Adarsha Hindu
  Hotel, Ichhamati.

MANIK BANDYOPADHYAY (1908-1956, b. Dumka)
Essentially a story teller, his novels achieved early fame with his realistic portrayal of the life of East Bengal. His vision is clear and at times even hard. Less concerned with the intellectual than with the psychological nuances of human character. His *Putul Nacher Itikatha* has been regarded by many critics as the most powerful psychological novel in recent Bengali literature.

Chief works: Divaratrir Kavya, Putul Nacher Itikatha, Padma Nadir
  Majhi, Atasimami, Pragaitihasik.

SARADINDU BANERJEE (b. 1899, Jaunpur)
A lawyer by profession, he soon left the Bar and devoted himself to writing. Gave up poetry in favour of short stories and novels. Unlike many writers of modern Bengal who are too serious, too subtle and too complex, he writes thrillers, detective fiction and light humorous stories. *Chief works*: Jhinder Bandi, Tikimedh, Rater Atithi.

TARASANKAR BANERJEE (b. 1898, Birbhum)
Was imprisoned for political activities in early youth. First published work was a collection of poems but soon turned to stories and novels. Developed an interest in the decadent zamindars of Bengal and has reflected their life with great truth and insight, but shows equal sympathy with peasant life. His keen social consciousness gave to some of his writing a propagandist bias but his recent writings combine purpose with devotion to the art of storytelling. Has the gift of creating an atmosphere with a few deft touches and also shows considerable powers of characterisation. Has won the Saratchandra Gold Medal, and the Rabindra Memorial Prize and the Sahitya Akademi Award.
Chief works: Ganadevata, Panchagram, Kalindi, Jalsaghar, Sandipan
                  Pathsala, Hansuli Banker Upakatha, Arogya Niketan,
                  Nagini Kanyar Kahini.

MANOJE BASU (b. 1901, Jessore)
Mainly a short story writer, his stories move us by their idyllic charm, refinement and delicacy. Specially successful with love stories of early youth.
Chief works: Narabandh, Banamarmar, Sainik, Navina Yatra, Plavan.

SANJAY BHATTACHARYA (b. 1909, Comilla)
Started as a lyric poet but soon took to writing stories and novels with deep social purpose. Has sought to blend reason and imagination with feeling and reflects the disintegration of society and personality which has marked the life of Bengal in recent decades.
Chief works: Aprem O Prem, Natun Din, Padavali, Dinanta, Phasal,
                Natun Diner Kahini.

PRAMATHANATH BISI (b. 1902, Rajshahi)
Poet and essayist with a sense of humour. Work often characterised by irony. Seeks to reflect the helplessness of man before nature and is a conscious and conscientious follower of Bernard Shaw in his dramas and of Thomas Hardy in his novels.
Chief works: Akuntala, Uttarmegh, Yuktaveni, Chalan Bil, Padma,
                Dynamite, Kamalakanter Asar.

BUDDHADEVA BOSE (b. 1908, Dacca)
One of the leading writers of contemporary Bengal who writes prose and poetry with equal facility and distinction. Established his reputation in early youth as a poet. Has edited *Kavita*, a journal of poetry, for almost twenty years. Was at first criticised by orthodox literary men for his views on sex and society, but is now accepted by both traditionalists and experimentalists. His work is sensuous and close to the earth and shows a strong lyrical element even in stories and novels.
Chief works: Bandir Bandana, Kankavati, Shiter Prarthana Vasanter Uttar, Basar Ghar, Lalmegh, Parikrama, Tithidor, Galpa-Sankalan, Asamanya Meye, Hathat Aler Jhalkani.

AMIYA CHAKRAVARTY (b. 1901)
Essentially a poet and seeks to reflect the new experiences which modern civilisation is bringing to the traditional culture of Bengal. Always trying out new techniques which, when successful, bring the atmosphere of far horizons into the closed life of the average Bengali.
Chief works: Ek Mutho, Khasra, Parapar, Pala Badal.

NIRENDRA NATH CHAKRAVARTY (b. 1924, Faridpur)
One of the most promising among the younger writers of Bengal. Has drawn the attention of critics by his sensibility and delicate use of words.
Chief works: Neel Niranjan, Ajab Jivika, Mukti Sangram.

JEEBANANANDA DAS (1899-1954, b. Barisal)
One of the most controversial poets of recent times, he attracted the attention of critics by the richness of his imagery and his subtle power of drawing music out of common words. Posthumously awarded the Rabindra Memorial Prize and also the Sahitya Akademi (National Academy of Letters) prize for the outstanding work in Bengali published between 1947-54.
Chief works: Jhara Palak, Dhusar Pandulipi, Banalata Sen, Sat-ti Tarar Timir.

SAJANI KANTA DAS (b. 1900, Burdwan)
Poet, writer and satirist, he dominated for some years the literary scene as a strong critic of ultra-modern tendencies. Has a vigorous intellect which he often uses for bitter and scathing satire. The editor of *Sanibarer Chiti*, and the President of the Bangiya Sahitya Parisad.
Chief works: Ajay, Akash Vasar, Madhu O Hul, Alo Andhari, Keds O Sandal, Bhav O Chhanda, Manas-saravar, Rajhansa.

SUDHINDRA NATH DATTA (b. 1901, Calcutta)
Known mainly as a poet, is also a critic of very fine perception. One of
the few Bengali poets who have consciously used scholarship as an
ingredient of poetry. His work has been compared to that of Eliot for its
intellectual and muscular quality.
Chief works: Svagata, Orchestra, Krandasi.

BISHNU DEY (b. 1909, Calcutta)
A poet of distinction, he has also tried his hand at literary criticism.
Starting as a symbolist, won recognition for the musical quality of
his poetry and his ability to produce effects with great economy of
words.
Chief works: Chora Bali, Purvalekha, Sandiper Char.

AJIT DUTTA (b. 1907, Dacca)
Essentially a poet, has also made a mark as an essay writer. His poems
have a rich sensuous quality and are noted for their lyrical spirit.
Chief works: Kushumer Mas, Punarnava, Janantike, Patal Kanya.

NARAYAN GANGOPADHYAYA (b. 1918, Dinajpur)
A young professor in Calcutta who prefers to hide behind this pen-name.
Essentially a story writer, has no sympathy with hyprocrisy whether
practised by the rich or the poor, by the townsman or the villager.
Chief works: Krishnapaksha, Janmantar, Trophee, Timir-tirtha, Vana-
joytsna, Vidisha, Suryasarathi, Svarnasita.

SANTOSH KUMAR GHOSH (b. 1920, Barisal)
Writer of short stories, novels and essays of distinction. Especially
successful in portraying the downward trend in the economic position
of the middle-classes of Bengal. His stories have both wit and sympathy.
Chief works: Chinemati, Paravat, Shuksari, Shrestha Galpa.

SUBODH GHOSH (b. 1909, Hazaribagh)
Has had a very rich experience of life and worked by turns as a performer
in a circus, a health inspector, a district board employee, a bus conductor,
a confectioner, a hotel keeper, a poultry farmer and a mica prospector!
Led for some time the life of a Muslim when he joined a gypsy gang.
Achieved fame overnight by a powerful story entitled 'Fossil'. His rich
experience of life, powerful language and deep social consciousness give
his stories a very distinctive flavour.
Chief works: Gangotri, Gramayamuna, Jatugriha, Tilanjali, Triyama,
Fossil, Bharat-prem Katha, Manikarnika, Satabhisha.

KAZI NAZRUL ISLAM (b. 1899, Burdwan)
Took the literary world of Bengal by storm by his poem 'Vidrohi'. Many regard him as the greatest poetic force in Bengali literature after Rabindranath Tagore. Hot, impetuous and extravagant, his poetry has many glaring defects, but has impressed the mind of Bengal by its sheer energy. Was hailed as *the* poet of the political movement in 1930. His works show the qualities of a true poet and a powerful prose writer.
Chief works: Agnivina, Sanchita, Dolan Champa, Chhayanat, Badhan Hara, Mrityu Kshudha, Jhilimili, Vyathar Dan, Rikter Vedan.

HUMAYUM KABIR (b. 1906, Faridpur)
Has made his mark in many fields: as poet, essayist, philosopher, administrator and parliamentarian. His prose is characterised by its intellectual quality. His poems brought a distinct note of comradeship and realism into the love poetry of Bengal. Editor of *Chaturanga*. Member of Sahitya Akademi. President, All India Writers Convention, Delhi, 1956.
Chief works: Sathi; Svapna Sadh; Mahatma and Other Poems; Men and Rivers; Banglar Kavya; The Indian Heritage; Science, Democracy and Islam; Marxvad; Education in New India.

ARUN MITRA (b. 1919)
One of the younger poets who has achieved distinction in recent times, his poems have an elusive and plaintive note.
Chief work: Utser Dike.

NARENDRANATH MITRA (b. 1916, Faridpur)
One of the most powerful among the present-day short story writers of Bengal, he shows great skill in capturing the atmosphere of a locality or presenting a character. Also notable for his sensitiveness to mood and situation. While conscious of the growing harshness of life among the middle-classes of Bengal, has a sense of deep sympathy with human suffering. His mastery of technique and his rich human feelings combine to give his stories great popularity among literary critics as well as the general reader.
Chief works: Asavarna, Ultorath, Godhuli, Durabhasini, Dhupkathi, Halde Bari.

PREMENDRA MITRA (b. 1904, Banaras)
One of the foremost poets, short story writers and essayists of contemporary Bengal, the quantity of his production is small but whatever he has written is marked by great depth of thought and distinction of langu-

age. Early writing was realistic and marked by deep sympathy with
the down and out. In recent years he shows a wider understanding of
various aspects of human nature, but his sympathy with the poor and
the downtrodden remains as strong as ever. Finds beauty and strength
even in poverty. Slums are for him, not merely a grim background for
tears and lamentations, but a real world with its own life, its own romance
and its own drama. Sahitya Akademi Award, 1957.

Chief works: Prathama, Samrat, Shrestha Kabita, Bhavikal, Benami
Bandar, Putul O Pratima, Michil, Saptapadi.

SAILAJANANDA MOOKERJEE (b. 1901, Burdwan)
One of the leaders of the movement which turned Bengali literature
towards a new and factual realism, he has from his earliest days written
about the half-starved and exploited proletariat of Bengal. Many of his
stories have the background of coalmines which he knows intimately.
Often brilliant in portrayal of types, and of a hard unrelenting environment, he is a writer of great creative power.

Chief works: Abhishap, Anath Ashram, Homanal, Atasi, Narimedh,
Din-majur.

ASOKE VIJAY RAHA (b. 1910, Sylhet)
There is a sense of robust faith and beauty in much of his writings and
he has used traditional forms with great skill.

Chief works: Udo Chithir Jhank, Dihang Nadir Banke, Bhanumatir
Math, Rakta Sandhya.

ANANDA SANKAR RAY (b. 1904, Orissa)
A brilliant writer, who has established his position through his short
stories, poems, essays and novels. A keen observer of men and manners,
his writing is marked by a rare lightness of touch and brilliant wit. While
there is intellectual clarity and balance in much of his writing, the emo-
tional current is never absent. A member of the Sahitya Akademi.

Chief works: Satyasatya, Agun Niye Khela, Putul Niye Khela, Asamapika,
Prakritir Parihas, Pathe Prabase, Rakhi, Ekti Vasanta.

PRABODH KUMAR SANYAL (b. 1907, Calcutta)
Has a passion for travelling and evokes in his writings the atmosphere
of the places he has visited. His stories and novels are charged with
this impact of a traveller's life and even the characters in his stories
and novels are restless and always on the move.

Chief works: Priya-Bandhavi, Maha Prasthaner Pathe, Anka-Banka,
Banahamsi, Hasu Banu, Yayavar.

ARUN KUMAR SARKAR (b. 1922, Krishnanagar)
A poet of distinction with a fine sensitiveness to words and moods.
Chief work: Durer Akash.

SUNIL CHANDRA SARKAR (b. 1907)
Has a light touch which he exploits in dealing with unusual themes and
incidents.
Chief work: *Milita* (a book of poems).

ACHINTYA KUMAR SEN GUPTA (b. 1903, Noakhali)
Made his reputation quite early as a poet and novelist with a strong
realist tendency. Wide experience of urban and rural life in East and
West Bengal has mellowed his early realism and supplied him with the
material of many stories and novels. His deep sympathy with poverty
and suffering gives a rich human tone to much of his writing.
Chief works: Amavasya, Priya o Prithivi, Bede, Pratham Prem, Chhini-
mini, Prachchhadpat, Asamudra, Diganta, Jatan Bibi.

GLOSSARY

Adivasi : literally, original inhabitants ; used for tribal people

ahimsa : nonviolence

akanda : a plant with white and purple blossoms

almirah : a cupboard, wardrobe or a bookcase

anna : coin, worth about 1¼ American cents, or about 1½ British pennies; sixteen annas equal one rupee

Asharh : third month of the Bengali year; corresponding to June 15 to July 15

babu : title of respect for a Hindu gentleman; master

betel : an Asiatic creeper. Its leaves, with a little shell lime, are wrapped around parings of the arecanut (which is, generally, thus called betelnut) and are chewed.

bhikshu : a Buddhist monk

binna : a wild shrub that grows waist high

brinjal : eggplant

bund : an artificial embankment

Chalukya : a dynasty that rose to power in South India in the 6th Century A.D.

champak : a fragrant, golden-coloured flower

dada : elderly respected person, literally older brother

dacoit : one of a class of robbers, often murderous, who act in gangs

dhoti : the long loincloth worn by Hindu men

didi : elder sister

Fa Hien : a famous Chinese traveller who visited India at the beginning of the 5th Century

florican : a bird in India of the bustard family

ganja : the tender parts of the hemp plant, smoked for its intoxicating effect

gazi badar, badar : cry used by boatmen plying their boats

285

ghat : a flight of steps leading to the riverside
ghee : clarified butter
godown : a warehouse
gur : molasses, coarse sugar
guru : teacher, especially a spiritual guide or preceptor

hasnu hana : a strongly scented flower that blooms at night
hubble-bubble : a smoking pipe in which the smoke is drawn through
    water before inhaling

Jain : a follower of the heterodox Hindu sect founded in the 6th Century
    B.C.
Jaishtha : second month in the Bengali calendar, May 15 to June 15
jarda : scented tobacco which is chewed
jhapan : a kind of sedan chair
jheel : a marsh or lake, particularly one left after a flood
Juhu : a beach on the Arabian Sea near Bombay

kadam : a flowering tree that blossoms during the rains
kapalik : a priest devoted to the worship of Kali, goddess of death and
    destruction
kash : elephant grass
kirtan : a devotional song, praising gods and goddesses
kurchi : a wild flower
Kurmi : one of an agricultural caste

lac : a resinous substance secreted by the lac insect. It is a raw material
    for paints, polishes and sealing wax, and is inflammable.
lakh : one hundred thousand
Lakshmi : goddess of grace and good fortune

Magh : tenth month of the Bengali year, corresponding to January 15
    to February 15
mahua : a flowering tree
maidan : an open space, esplanade or parade ground
mantra,s : incantation of sacred texts; also ritualistic spell
maund : weight measure, in Bengal about 82 pounds
megh-mallar : well-known tune invoking the rains
mia : title of respect for a Muslim gentleman
Mimamsa : a school of thought in Hindu philosophy which seeks salva-
    tion through a method of religious dialectics and devotion
minar : turret or tower

Padma : a river in eastern Bengal
pakur : large, branching tree
pan : betel leaf, often prepared for chewing
papadum : wafer-thin bread, may be salted or spiced
Pashupatinath : a name for Siva
Paus : ninth month of the Bengali year, corresponding to December 15
    to January 15
peepal tree : large, branching fig tree, regarded as sacred
Phalgun : eleventh month of the Bengali year, corresponding to February
    15 to March 15
pice : Indian coin, equal to one-fourth of an anna
pie : smallest Indian coin, equal to one-twelfth of an anna
Prakrit : Aryan vernacular dialects of India as distinguished from Sans-
    krit
puja : a Hindu's worship of, or homage to, the gods

raga : a mode, an arrangement of intervals which defines a melody
rath : a car or chariot, especially one used to carry an image of a god
Ratnakar : a notorious robber who became a holy man known as Val-
    miki
rupee : Indian coin, equal to sixteen annas, worth approximately 21
    U.S. cents and 1s. 6d. in English currency

sadhu : a Hindu ascetic or holy man
sal : a tall tree noted for hard wood
sannyasi, sanyashi, sanyasi : ascetic, mendicant
Santal : tribal people, agriculturalists, chiefly in the hill country of
    Bengal-Bihar border areas
Saraswati : goddess of learning, music and speech
saree, sari : the principal garment of a Hindu woman
seer : measure of weight, approximately 2 lbs.
sephali : a flower that falls from the tree at night
Shastric : pertaining to the Hindu scriptures, the Shastra
stupa : a religious mound or tower, often containing a relic and usually
    Buddhist
swami, swamiji : an honorific title, added to a name; lord, king, the
    reverend (as applied to a religious teacher)

tantrik : having to do with the tantras, Hindu religious works; chiefly
    of a magical or mystical nature. Also Buddhist works of similar
    character.
tapasya : devotion, asceticism

teapoy : small three-legged table, a tea table
tulsi : the holy basil, grown as a sacred plant in many Hindu homes
Turi : one of the tribal groups in India

Valmiki : according to legend, the first great poet of Sanskrit, a holy
   man who was once a notorious robber named Ratnakar
veena, vina : ancient Hindu stringed musical instrument of the lyre
   type, still very popular
vihara : monastery

zamindar : a landowner